Y11

SALT... ...E

SCIENCE

GCSE Volume 2
Year 11 Units

Contents

About this book

Salters GCSE Science has been written for your GCSE course. Teachers and examiners have written the book to help you learn about science and prepare for your exams.

We hope that you will enjoy using the books, learning about science and how it affects you.

To help you find your way around the book it has been divided into ten units. There is also a section on understanding the final examinations, which come at the end of the course.

Units

Each unit starts with an introductory page. Read this page to get a feel for some of the things you will be learning about in the unit. There are also some questions to try before you start so that you can find out how much you already know.

Double-page spreads

The material you need to study has been divided up into double-page spreads to help you find your way around. Here are some of the things you will come across on the double-page spreads:

Words in bold type are important scientific terms. Make sure that you understand what they mean. You may find that it helps to make a list of these words when you come to revise.

Things to do box

Things to do

When you come across a box like this it will contain questions or other tasks for you to complete. Answering questions will help you to check your understanding.

Fact box

A box like this will contain important scientific facts. Make sure that you know and understand everything that appears in these boxes.

Higher tier box

Material in a box like this will only be tested in the higher tier exams. Check with your teacher to find out which exam you are entered for.

Student sheet symbol

This symbol means that you may be asked to do an activity or worksheet to help with your study. Your teacher will decide which sheets you will need.

At the end of each unit you will find plenty of questions to test what you have understood. These questions are similar to the type of questions that you may be asked in your exams. Remember, practice makes perfect.

Understanding examinations

This section, by an experienced Salters' examiner, helps you to understand what the final examinations will be like. Sample answers are included to show you how you can get maximum credit for what you know by matching your answers to the instructions in the questions.

We hope you enjoy using the books.

The Salters GCSE science team.

INTRODUCING
Seeing inside the body

Try these first

1 The _____ of a wave is the number of waves per second and is measured in ____.

2 The length of a complete wave is called its _____.

3 We can find the speed of a wave from an equation that uses your last two answers. The equation is speed = _____.

4 Atoms are made from _____ , _____ and _____.

5 The part at the centre of an atom is called its _____ and contains particles called _____ and _____.

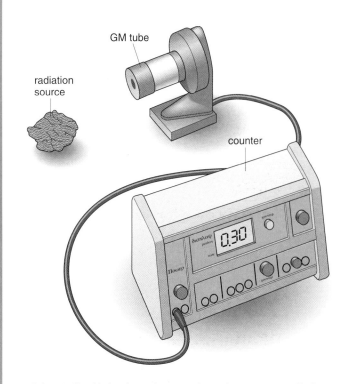

A Geiger-Müller (GM) tube and counter is used to measure radiation.

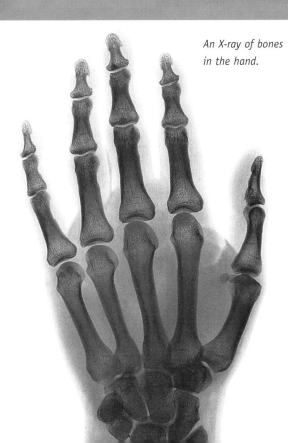

An X-ray of bones in the hand.

In this unit you will learn:

- about X-rays and X-ray machines
- about the variety of different types of radiation and how some types are used in health care
- that radioactivity comes from the nucleus of atoms
- about α, β and γ radiation
- about background radiation and where it comes from
- the dangers of radiation from radioactive materials
- how γ radiation can be used to treat cancer
- what is meant by half-life
- how radioactivity can be used to date rocks
- about some other uses for radioactive materials.

1 The beginnings of medical physics

Is there something wrong inside me?

 SB1

When you are not well, the doctor can get some information about what is wrong from external signs (for example, spots) or measurements like your temperature or blood pressure. However, the doctor will often need to know what is happening inside your body.

One way to find out would be to cut you open! Sometimes 'exploratory' operations are done, but they are unpleasant, inconvenient and expensive. If only there was some way to 'see inside the body' without cutting it open!

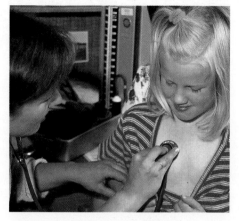

A doctor examines a patient using a stethoscope.

Röntgen to the rescue

An answer to this problem came from research in another area of science. Wilhelm Röntgen, a German scientist, was investigating the passage of electricity through gases. He was working with a glass tube that had gas at low pressure inside it and a high voltage connected across it. A screen coated with a fluorescent material glowed when put near the tube. He realised that some unknown rays must be coming from the tube.

Röntgen experimented with lots of different things between the tube and the screen.

He found that he could see a 'shadow picture' of the bones in his hand. The surrounding flesh showed up as a faint outline. He published his findings in *Nature* in January 1896. Röntgen called the rays 'X-rays', and within a few months, doctors were using his discovery.

Wilhelm Röntgen won the Nobel Prize for Physics in 1901 for his discovery of X-rays.

Making use of X-rays

X-rays affect photographic film in a similar way to light. The more X-rays that reach the film, the darker it goes. As X-rays pass through substances, they are absorbed more by denser materials. For example, bone stops more of the rays than soft flesh, so on a medical X-ray, the bones show up lighter than the flesh around them.

As well as medical uses, X-rays are used to look inside things such as luggage at airports.

Some good effects, some bad effects!

 SB2

X-rays carry a lot of energy and can damage body cells. Dangers from X-rays are **cumulative** – they add up – so lots of small doses can build up to cause damage.

 When X-rays pass through living cells, they can cause damage by knocking electrons out from atoms of substances in the cells. This is called **ionisation**, because atoms or molecules which are electrically charged are called ions.

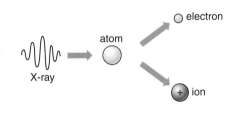

Ionisation of an atom by an X-ray.

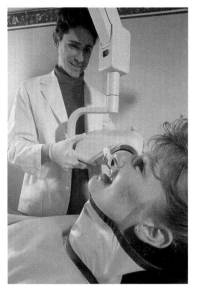

This patient is protected by a lead apron while the dentist takes an X-ray of her teeth.

If cells get exposed to a lot of X-rays in a short period of time, enough ions can be formed to permanently damage the cell and it dies. This is called *acute* cell damage. The dose of X-rays given to patients is carefully controlled to make sure this never happens. However, exposure to repeated low doses of X-rays can cause changes that eventually build up to cause long-term damage. This long-term damage is called *chronic* damage.

One way in which ionisation can affect a cell is by changing the cell's DNA. The cell might simply die, but it could also grow and divide much more quickly than normal. The clump of cells formed when this happens is called a **tumour**.

Changes in the DNA in a cell are called **mutations**. Other causes of mutation include background radiation from rocks or from space and some chemicals. Not all mutations are harmful. Some lead to changes in the growth of cells or whole organisms which make them more successful. Such changes are thought to play a part in evolution.

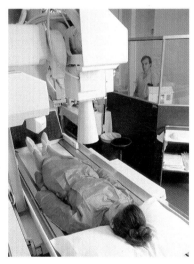

The radiographer stands behind a lead glass window to minimise his exposure to X-rays.

Things to do

Doctors have to balance the risk to patients against the benefits. X-rays help the diagnosis of tumours, broken bones and other problems without the need for operations.

1   Make a list of things which can be done to reduce risks to patients and operators in hospital X-ray departments.

2   Find out why X-ray operators wear badges like this one.

A radiation badge.

What is radiation? (SS) SB3

There are many types of radiation. In each case the radiation travels from a **source** to a **detector**. As it travels outwards the radiation will become more spread out so that its strength becomes less. When you speak the sound waves are the radiation and they are detected by an ear or a microphone.

Some types of radiation can be dangerous. If your skin receives too much ultraviolet radiation from the Sun it can be damaged, and so we use a Sun block cream to stop it.

The television can be controlled by pressing buttons on the handset. This handset sends out infrared radiation.

Radiation all around you

The most dangerous types of radiation are called **ionising radiation**, because they carry enough energy to alter atoms in their path. A detector called a Geiger-Müller, or GM, counter can measure the electric charges produced by ionising radiation. Wherever you try this, you will find that some radiation, called **background radiation**, is always there.

The actual values will vary quite a lot depending on where you live. You can get a reading in the air.

You will also get a small reading from some foods, especially the ones that contain a lot of potassium – 'Lo-Salt' is a good example.

This light meter can detect light radiation.

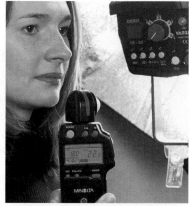

When the light is turned on, the meter reading changes.

Some rocks will produce a high count whilst others are not radioactive at all. Luminous paint on old clocks and watches can also produce quite a high reading.

All of this may seem to be a worry but notice that almost all of it is completely natural and normal. Since some of the radiation comes from rocks, those of you that live in areas where there are certain types of rock, such as granite, will have a bigger count rate for the background radiation.

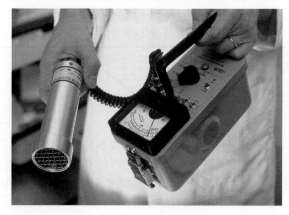

A GM counter can detect ionising radiation.

Where does background radiation come from?

As you can see, only a tiny fraction of this radiation comes from artificial sources.

Radon gas SB4

Many types of soil, bricks and stone contain small amounts of uranium. This is **radioactive,** and produces a gas called radon, which is also radioactive. Outdoors, it is quickly dispersed, but it can build up in cellars and caves.

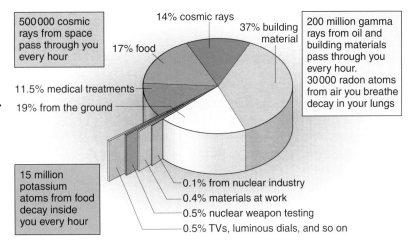

500 000 cosmic rays from space pass through you every hour

14% cosmic rays

17% food

37% building material

200 million gamma rays from oil and building materials pass through you every hour.
30 000 radon atoms from air you breathe decay in your lungs

11.5% medical treatments

19% from the ground

15 million potassium atoms from food decay inside you every hour

0.1% from nuclear industry
0.4% materials at work
0.5% nuclear weapon testing
0.5% TVs, luminous dials, and so on

Chart showing sources of background radiation.

In areas such as Cornwall there is more uranium in the rocks so new buildings are designed with fans to ventilate the foundations and remove the gas.

This radiation is always there. In experiments on radioactivity you need to measure the background radiation and subtract it from each result.

Measuring the dose

Radiation can be measured in counts per second. One count per second is known as a becquerel (Bq). The problem with this is that there is more than one sort of radiation from radioactive materials. If you are measuring the radiation received by a person it is better to use a unit called the sievert (Sv) which also takes into account which sort of radiation is involved and how it affects the body organs. This is a big unit and we usually work in millisieverts (mSv = $\frac{1}{1000}$ Sv) or in microsieverts (μSv = $\frac{1}{1000\,000}$ Sv).

The average person in the UK gets an annual dose of about 2500 μSv from background radiation but this will vary a lot depending on where the person lives, their job and what they eat.

optional fan

air space

membrane

air brick

The foundations of buildings built on ground with a high amount of uranium contain fans to remove any radon gas.

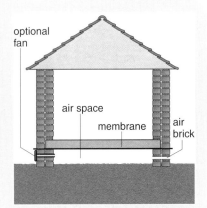

Things to do

1   Use the pie chart to find:
    a The biggest source of background radiation.
    b What % of the radiation comes from the nuclear industry.

2   The average annual dose for a person in the UK is 2500 Sv. Use a calculator and the percentage figures on the chart to make a table showing the dose received from each source.

3   Make a list of jobs where you think the workers will be exposed to more than the average radiation dose. In each case suggest where the radiation is coming from.

Radon doses in Britain: the higher the peak the larger the dose.

Becquerel discovers radioactivity

Henri Becquerel was the professor of Physics at the École Polytechnique in Paris. One day, he left a rock on top of a photographic plate which was wrapped in black paper. Later, when he used the plate, he found that it had been exposed to some radiation. He had discovered a form of invisible radiation that could get through the paper and affect the plate.

Becquerel thought that the rays must be similar to X-rays which had recently been discovered. He had discovered radioactivity but it was Pierre and Marie Curie who made the next important discovery about radioactivity.

Becquerel's historic experiment can be repeated by leaving a radioactive source locked inside a radioactivity safe with a piece of film wrapped round it.

Becquerel shared the Nobel Prize for Physics with the Curies in 1903.

The Curies

Pierre Curie was making discoveries about magnetism at the Sorbonne in Paris where, in 1895, he married Maria Sklodowska. Maria did research into the rays that Becquerel had discovered.

In 1898 she found that they also came from a uranium ore called pitchblende. From this ore the Curies managed to get small quantities of two previously unknown radioactive elements, polonium and radium. They were awarded the Nobel Prize for Physics in 1903 together with Henri Becquerel.

Marie continued to work on radioactivity and X-rays and received the Nobel Prize for Chemistry in 1911. The dangers of the radiation were not known then and she died in 1934 from leukaemia caused by the radiation. Her daughter, Irène, married Frederick Joliot and they also carried out important research and discovered artificial radioactivity in 1934.

Pierre Curie was killed in a road accident in 1906. Marie took over his job at the Sorbonne and became the first woman teacher at the university.

Things to do

Use CD ROM encyclopedias or the Internet to find out more about these important scientists. Make a short presentation to your class saying how their discoveries have affected our lives.

Radioactivity and the atom

The radioactivity that Becquerel discovered is different from all other types, because it comes from the **nuclei** of atoms (X-rays are caused by movement of electrons in atoms). You learnt something about the structure of atoms in the unit *Electricity in the home* (Y10), but to understand about radioactivity, you need to learn more about atoms.

About atoms (SS) SB5, SB6

Atoms are made up of small particles:

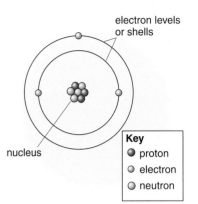

The particles that make up an atom.

- electrons, which have a negative electric charge

- protons, which have a positive electric charge

- neutrons which have no charge (neutral).

The protons and neutrons cluster together at the centre of the atom and form its nucleus. The nucleus is heavy, very small and positively charged. The electrons occupy the rest of the space of the atom.

It is a little difficult to imagine how much empty space there is in an atom but if the nucleus was the size of a football then the whole atom might be the size of Wembley Stadium with the electrons spinning through the stands.

The **chemistry** of an atom depends on the number of electrons. Each element has a different number of electrons in its atoms to

Particle	Mass (atomic units)	Charge	Position in atom
proton (p)	1	+1	nucleus
neutron (n)	1	0	nucleus
electron (e)	$\frac{1}{1840}$ (almost 0)	−1	levels round nucleus

give it different chemical properties. The number of electrons must match the number of protons in the nucleus. This means that each element has its own **proton number**, sometimes called the **atomic number**.

The **atomic mass number** is found by adding the number of protons and neutrons in the nucleus. The mass of the electrons is so small that we don't include it.

However, it can sometimes happen that the atoms of an element do not all contain the same number of neutrons. For example, all carbon atoms contain 6 protons, and most contain 6 neutrons, but a few have 8 neutrons, giving an atomic mass of 14. Different forms of the same element are called **isotopes**.

F

The atomic mass and atomic number (proton number) of an element are shown by putting them in front of the symbol, like this:

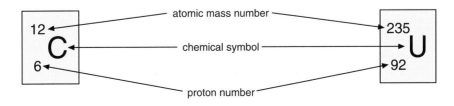

4 What is radioactivity?

The combination of protons and neutrons in some isotopes of some elements makes the nucleus of the atoms unstable. These unstable nuclei break down (**decay**), releasing radiation. The element is said to be **radioactive**.

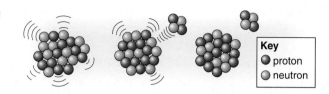

Key
● proton
○ neutron

Large amounts of energy are released in radioactive decay of atoms, so the radiation is very dangerous – it is ionising radiation. To avoid danger from radioactive materials, it is useful to know how far the radiation can spread!

How far does it spread?

 SB7

A GM tube linked to a counter can be used to measure the radiation at different distances from a **radioactive source**.

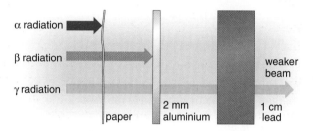

α radiation
β radiation
γ radiation
weaker beam
paper
2 mm aluminium
1 cm lead

This shows the penetrating power of different types of radiation.

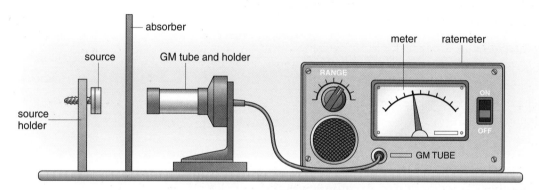

absorber
source
GM tube and holder
meter   ratemeter
source holder
RANGE
ON
OFF
GM TUBE

An experiment to test the properties of radiation from different radioactive sources.

The radiation from different sources is not always the same. There are three different types of radioactivity and they behave in different ways.

Remember that as the radiation travels further from its source it will become more spread out and will seem weaker – so the main safety factor is distance.

Each of these radiations comes from the **nucleus** of an atom. Which type is produced depends on the exact particles in the nucleus. Some, like americium-241, will emit more than one sort of radiation.

Type of radiation	What stops it	How far does it spread in air
Alpha (α)	thick paper	a few mm
Beta (β)	a few mm of aluminium	1–2 m
Gamma (γ)	several cm of lead	many metres

More about α, β and γ

Alpha radiation is made of particles. Each particle is made from two protons and two neutrons – just the same as the nucleus of a helium atom. When it leaves the nucleus at high speed, it is as heavy as a small atom and goes out in a straight line. It knocks bits off other atoms as it goes and creates a lot of ions. With each collision it slows down until it stops, then it picks up two stray electrons and becomes an atom of helium. Alpha radiation is particularly dangerous because it creates so many ions in a very short distance.

Alpha (α) particle.

The protons give each alpha particle a positive charge so that it will move towards the negative and away from the positive in an electric field.

Beta radiation is actually high speed electrons that are emitted from the nucleus. Electrons are much smaller than atoms so they will get further between collisions and penetrate further. Each collision creates ions but these are much more spread out than those from alpha particles. As the electron slows down the collisions make it change direction more and more and its path is wavy and unpredictable.

Beta (β) particle.

The moving beta particles are negatively charged and will be attracted towards the positive (+) and repelled by the negative (−) of an electric field – the opposite way to alpha. Magnetic fields also deflect beta particles the opposite way to alpha.

Gamma radiation is not particles at all but short bursts of electromagnetic waves. There is no charge on these waves so they are not deflected by either magnetic or electric fields.

Gamma (γ) radiation.

The waves can easily pass through materials unless they make a direct hit on an atom. When this happens the large energy in the waves ionises the atom.

Gamma radiation can be dangerous because it is so penetrating that it causes damage deep inside things. It can be deceiving too, because a lot of it goes straight through detectors like GM tubes without any collisions, so there often seems to be less of it than there really is. Thick concrete or heavy metal shielding is needed to stop the rays.

? Things to do

1. What is the link between distance from the source and the intensity of the radiation?

2. Radioactive sources are kept in special boxes.

   a What do you think the boxes should be made of?

   b Where should they be kept?

3. 🖥 Use the information on this page to make a fact table about α, β and γ radiation. Use a computer program, such as *Word* or *Excel*, to set up your table.

Radioactive processes happen in the nucleus of atoms (unlike chemical reactions which use the outer electrons). The nucleus of a radioactive isotope is not stable. It can become more stable by giving out a particle (either α or β). At the same time, it releases a lot of energy as γ radiation. The change is called a **radioactive decay**. The number of protons in the nucleus is changed, so what is left is now an atom of a *different* element!

If you remember that the **total charge** and **mass** will remain the same, you can balance the equations for decay and work out what must happen.

Alpha emission (SS) SB8, SB9

The particle that is emitted is made from 2 protons and 2 neutrons. The nucleus therefore loses these particles and becomes an atom of a new element *two places lower* in the Periodic Table and with a *mass 4 units less*.

$$\text{alpha} = {}^{4}_{2}\alpha$$

This equation shows what happens when a uranium-238 atom emits an alpha particle. Check what happens to the total of the mass and then the charge on each side. The equation is balanced.

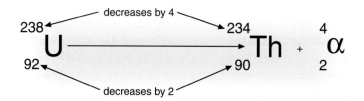

The new atom that is created is called the **daughter product**. You can find which daughter product is formed by looking up the new mass number on a Periodic Table.

Beta emission

In this case the particle given out is an electron. The mass of the electron is almost zero so the new atom has the same mass number as before. The electron has a charge of −1 and the total charges must remain the same so the new atom has an atomic number that is *one greater*. It is *one place higher* in the Periodic Table. It is as though one of its neutrons has split into a proton and an electron.

$$\text{beta} = {}^{0}_{-1}\beta$$

This equation shows what happens when strontium-90 emits an electron. Check again what happens to the total of the mass and then the charge on each side.

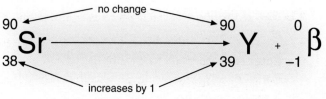

Decay series

Sometimes the daughter product from an α or β decay is also radioactive. It will decay in turn. Sometimes there will be a whole series of radioactive decays until finally a stable end-product is formed.

More about isotopes

We now know that most elements have more than one isotope. For example, most uranium atoms have mass number 238 (92 protons and 146 neutrons). However, a few (about 7 in every 1000) have only 143 neutrons, so their mass number is only 235. This isotope (uranium-235, also written as ^{235}U) decays by fission (splitting almost in half). Fission releases so much energy it was used in the first atomic bombs!

If you look at the Periodic Table, you will see that the relative atomic mass of chlorine is 35.5. Have you ever wondered about that 0.5? Chlorine is a mixture of two isotopes, with three atoms of chlorine-35 for every one of chlorine-37. Can you work out how this mixture gives an average mass of 35.5?

Using isotopes to date rocks

Some igneous rocks contain uranium, a radioactive element which decays through a series of stages, finally forming isotopes of lead. By careful comparison of the amount of uranium left with the amount of different lead isotopes, it is possible to measure the age of the rock.

Some other igneous rocks contain potassium. One of the isotopes of potassium (potassium-40) decays to form argon, which is trapped in the rock. As time goes by, the amount of potassium-40 gets less, and argon builds up. It takes about 1300 million years for half of the potassium-40 to decay away, so careful comparison of the amounts of potassium-40 and argon can indicate the age of very old rocks.

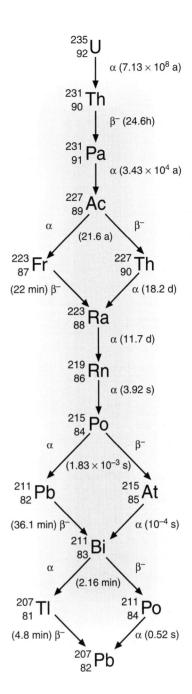

Things to do

(Use the Periodic Table to find proton numbers and symbols for some of these elements.)

1 What is special about technicium–99 that makes it useful for medical purposes?

2 Write decay equations for each of the following:

   a alpha-emitters: americium-241   radium-226   radon-222

   b beta emitters: iodine-131   carbon-14   caesium-137

3 Polonium-214 is part of a decay series that ends with lead-206, which is stable. The emission from polonium-214 is alpha, followed by beta, beta again, and finally another alpha emission. Write decay equations for each of these stages in the series, and name the element formed at each stage.

Radioactivity is a random process

Radioactive materials are not like light bulbs or X-ray machines. The radiation they emit cannot be turned on or off. It comes from inside the nucleus of the atom, where it is not affected by any external conditions. Radioactivity is a random process. You cannot watch an individual atom and predict when it will decay.

It is a bit like the situation with traffic accidents. You can't predict exactly who will be hurt in a traffic accident, or when, but you know that some accidents will happen – and the more traffic there is, the more accidents are likely. In the same way with radiation, the intensity of radiation depends on the size of the sample.

Measuring radioactive decay

 SB10

The rate at which a radioactive substance decays away will be quicker at first, then get slower and slower. The figures in this table show results for the decay of a sample of protoactinium.

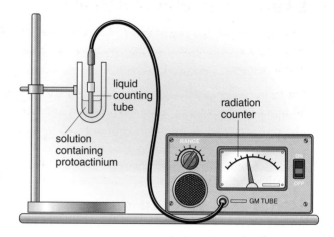

An experiment to measure the decay of protoactinium using a liquid GM tube.

Time (s)	0	30	60	90	120	150	180	210	240
Count rate (s⁻¹)	1000	725	535	415	320	225	175	125	95

The count rate (number of counts per second) is a measure of the activity. Use these results to plot a graph of activity against time. Put the time on the *x*-axis.

Working out the half-life

Whatever radioactive substance you measure, the general shape of the graph will always be the same. As the substance decays it is turned into a different material and the activity decreases as less of the radioactive material is left.

Choose any point near the start of the graph. Go along the graph until the count rate has halved. Check how long this took. Repeat this from your new point and see how long it takes to halve again.

No matter where you start from the time taken to halve the count rate is the same. This is called the **half-life**.

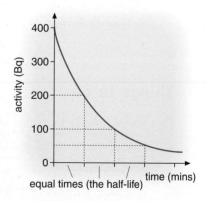

Decay graph showing the half-life of protoactinium.

Each different material has its own half-life. Some are very unstable and decay away quickly (short half-life), others decay much more slowly.

- The intensity of radiation at any time is directly proportional to the amount of the substance remaining.
- However big the sample, the time taken for half of it to decay away (the **half-life**) is always the same.
- Each different radioactive isotope has its own different half-life.

Using ideas about half-life

You can always find the amount of a substance left after a number of half-lives by using a simple flow chart. Between these times you would need to draw a graph or make a careful estimate.

For example, a source has activity of 1000 counts per second and a half-life of 20 minutes. What will the activity be after one hour?

$$1000 \text{ c/s} \xrightarrow{\text{20 mins}} 500 \text{ c/s} \xrightarrow{\text{20 mins}} 250 \text{ c/s} \xrightarrow{\text{20 mins}} 125 \text{ c/s}$$

So after 1 hour the activity will have fallen to just 125 counts per second. There will still be nearly the same amount of material left, but most of it has changed into a different element.

Knowing about half-lives helps you to choose the right material for a particular use. Schools choose radioactive sources with long half-lives. This gives less intense radiation (safer!) and means the effect will last a long time. In some medical uses, when radioactive material is put inside a patient, it is important that the radiation fades away quickly, so sources with very short half-lives are chosen.

Things to do

1 For hospital tests a patient needs to swallow a liquid with an activity of 512 becquerels. The liquid is prepared 8 hours earlier and has a half-life of 4 hours. What activity must it be when prepared?

2 An engineer puts some radioactive liquid into a pipeline to try and trace a leak. What sort of half-life might be suitable? What sort of emitter should the source be?

3 Cobalt-60 is used to treat cancers. Why is it important that it has a fairly long half-life?
Why should the hospital keep a careful record of its age?

4   Am-241, Sr-90 and Co-60 are commonly kept in schools as demonstration sources. Use the Internet or a CD ROM encyclopedia to find their half-lives. Why are these suitable?

7 Using radioactive material safely

Contamination and irradiation

 SB12, SB13

If a radioactive material is allowed to spread or spill out, the surroundings may be **contaminated**, for example, radioactive dust may be breathed in, or liquid spilt onto the skin. The danger remains until the contamination is washed off or removed. Because of this, radioactive materials for schools are in closed sources, so that material cannot escape.

If you are near to, but not touching, a radioactive source, you receive radiation – you are irradiated.

Things which have been irradiated do not become radioactive themselves. For example, some surgical instruments are irradiated to kill bacteria, but they are perfectly safe to use afterwards.

Risks from irradiation can be reduced by keeping exposure short, and working at a distance, using small robots or remote handling tools. Radioactive materials are kept in safe stores, with a label outside to warn of the hazard.

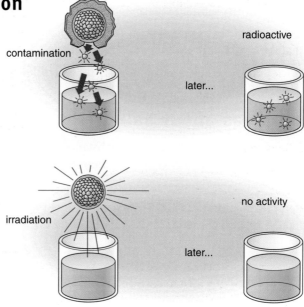

Contaminated material contains radioactivity, whereas irradiated material is only exposed to radiation, and does not remain active.

The radiation hazard symbol.

Uses of radioactive materials

There are lots of uses for radioactive materials.

- Tracers are used to track where chemicals or other materials go. The photograph shows a scientist who has put a small amount of a radioactive liquid into a river. She is now checking to find out where the currents have carried the liquid. The information will help people decide where it is safe to allow waste outlets.

- Leaks in a pipeline can be traced by adding a radioactive material to the liquid in the pipe. A GM counter is used to follow the progress of the liquid through the pipe.

- Welds in a pipe can be checked using a gamma source such as Co-60 on one side of the pipe to expose a photographic plate on the other side. When the film is developed it will show cracks in the weld in a similar way to an X-ray.

A scientist collects samples to check for the presence of radioactive material.

- The thickness of metal sheets can be measured, using a β source on one side of the sheet and a detector on the other. If the sheet is too thin, less radiation is absorbed and the machinery can be automatically adjusted to return to the correct thickness.

- Smoke detectors use a small radioactive source to ionise the air between two metal plates. The ions allow a small current to flow between the plates. Smoke particles attach themselves to the ions so that the current becomes smaller. The change in current is detected and sets off the alarm.

- Salt made from Na-24 can be included in salt solution. The solution has then been **labelled**. If this is injected into the blood stream its progress can be followed to help locate blood clots.

- Medical instruments can be **sterilised** by irradiation from a γ source so that any living material is killed. Hypodermic needles can be sterilised in this way after packing and sealing.

- Some cancers can be treated by irradiating the cancer cells with γ radiation to kill the cells. The rest of the body must be shielded from too large a dose. This is done by rotating the source round the patient. The beam always passes through the cancer area but the rest gets a lower dose.

Radioactive materials are used widely in industry, for instance in checking for leaks and ensuring secure welding in a pipeline.

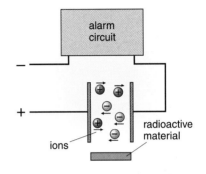

Cross-section through a smoke detector to show how radioactive material is used to make it work.

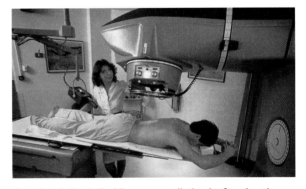

A patient is treated with gamma radiation by focusing the beam on the cancer and shielding the rest of the body.

Things to do

1 Why might an engineer use a γ source rather than X-rays to check the welds in a pipe?

2 Here is a list of applications using radioactive sources. Copy and complete the table, using a data book to find the type of emission from each source. Which of the sources in the table would be most suitable in each case?

a measuring the thickness of thin aluminium

b the source in a smoke detector

c testing for wear in engine parts

d investigating the digestive system with a salt solution.

Source	Emission	Half-life
Cs-137		28 years
Am-241		460 years
Tc-99		6 years
Na-24		15 hours
Fe-59		45 days

Thermography

The surface temperature of your body can give information about what is happening under the skin. For example, rheumatoid arthritis is a disease that damages joints. This causes friction as the bones move, so raising the temperature. A camera that is sensitive to infrared radiation, linked to a computer, can produce an image showing differences in temperature as different colours on a screen.

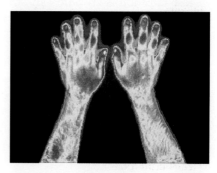

This thermograph shows the temperature difference over the surface of the hands.

Magnetic resonance imaging (MRI)

MRI was invented in the 1980s. It is painless, and as far as we know, harmless.

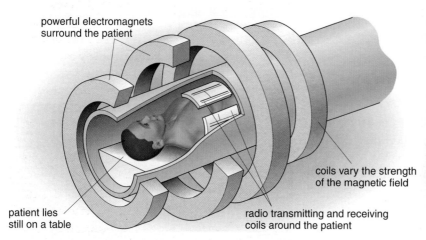

powerful electromagnets surround the patient

coils vary the strength of the magnetic field

patient lies still on a table

radio transmitting and receiving coils around the patient

A patient moves through a magnetic field and the effect of this on the body is recorded by the MRI machine, which produces an image of the body.

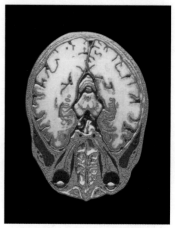

The internal structure of the brain is clear in this MRI scan of the skull.

The patient lies on a table which moves through a powerful electromagnet. The nuclei of hydrogen atoms in water in the body are affected by the magnetic field. A radio wave is passed through the body and it disturbs the alignment of some of the hydrogen atoms. As they flip back into position again, they emit radio waves of a slightly different frequency. The machine can detect where these waves have come from and gradually build up a picture of the organs within the body.

The electromagnetic spectrum (SS) SB14

Both infrared waves and radio waves are part of a wide range of radiations that make up the electromagnetic spectrum. The chart on the opposite page shows some of the different types of electromagnetic radiation, and some of their uses. If you have studied *Communicating information* (Y10), you will already know something about these radiations.

Radio waves Long wave (LW) and medium wave (MW) radio waves are used to carry radio broadcasts. The waves can spread round obstacles so your radio can pick them up even if you can't see the transmitter.

Short wave (SW) radio waves are used for shorter distance radio links, like police radio and CB. VHF means very high frequency and UHF means ultra high frequency (compared with other radio waves). These are used for high-quality stereo radio transmissions and for television. For good VHF and UHF reception, you need a clear route from your aerial to the transmitter.

X-rays

These are produced by specially designed X-ray machines. They can pass through skin and muscle but not so easily through bone. So X-rays can be used to take a shadow picture of the inside of your body. However, X-rays damage living cells and so a large X-ray dose can be harmful.

Gamma rays

These come from some radioactive substances. They pass easily through most materials and can damage living cells. Gamma ray sources must be handled with great care.

Microwaves These are very short wavelength radio waves. They are now used instead of cables for many telephone links. There has to be a direct line without any obstacles from the transmitter to the receiving dish. You may notice microwave receiving dishes on high masts near your home. Some microwaves are absorbed strongly by water and they heat it up. This is how microwave ovens heat food.

Infrared waves

These are given out by every hot object. Your body emits long wavelength infrared waves. The hotter the object, the shorter the infrared wavelength it emits. A red-hot electric fire element is hot enough to emit short wavelength infrared rays along with some visible red light.

Visible light

Sunlight is a mixture of infrared waves, visible light and ultraviolet waves. Ultraviolet waves cause a chemical reaction which tans the skin. It is dangerous to expose your skin to too many ultraviolet waves as they increase the risk of skin cancer.

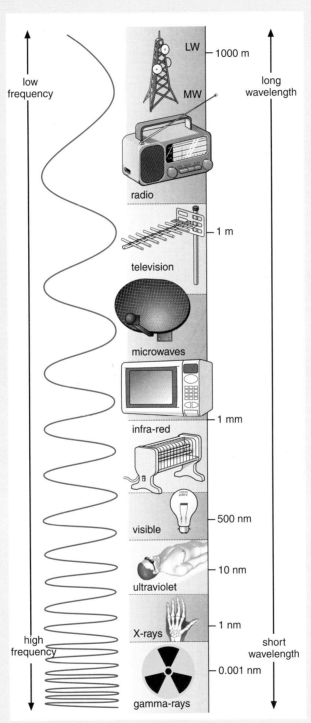

low frequency

long wavelength

LW — 1000 m

MW

radio

1 m

television

microwaves

1 mm

infra-red

500 nm

visible

10 nm

ultraviolet

1 nm

X-rays

high frequency

short wavelength

0.001 nm

gamma-rays

Changing theories

In early times people had no real idea of what light was.

In 1675 Isaac Newton said that he thought light was made from tiny particles given out by luminous objects. His theory explained the facts that were known at the time.

In 1678 a Dutch scientist, Christiaan Huygens, also explained all the facts by saying that light was made of lots of waves with a very short wavelength but Newton was more famous and his ideas were accepted for the next hundred years.

In 1802 Thomas Young showed that light could make an interference pattern similar to the pattern when ripples cross and that light must therefore be waves. This meant that Huygens was right!

In the 1860s James Maxwell did calculations to show that light could be an **electromagnetic wave** made from vibrating electric and magnetic fields and that this sort of wave could travel through a vacuum.

Light of different colours is made of waves of different wavelengths. We now know that there are electromagnetic waves of both longer and shorter wavelength, although our eyes are not sensitive to them.

The English scientist Isaac Newton made many contributions to science and was knighted in 1705.

Different colours seen in a soap bubble show areas of different thickness.

An equation for waves

Electromagnetic waves, like all other waves, must obey the wave equation:

wave speed = frequency × wavelength

or v = f × λ

A gamma source emits waves with a wavelength of 1×10^{-12} m and a frequency of 3×10^{20} Hz.

$v = f \times \lambda$

    $= 3 \times 10^{20} \times 1 \times 10^{-12}$

    $= 3 \times 10^{8}$ m/s

This example is done in 'standard form'. This makes very big or very small numbers easier to use. You write each number between 1 and 10 and then say how many times it has to be multiplied by 10 to get the number that you want. So 3×10^{20} really means 3 multiplied by 10, twenty times, so it is the same as 300 000 000 000 000 000 000.

If the power of 10 is negative then you divide by 10, that many times.

Carrying energy

A beam of electromagnetic radiation is made up of small packets of waves called photons. Waves with a greater frequency are vibrating faster and each photon carries more energy. The frequency of ultraviolet waves gives enough energy to damage cells, so too much sun can cause skin cancers. X-rays and gamma rays will need even greater care as they have even bigger frequency.

The electromagnetic spectrum

As the frequency of electromagnetic waves increases from small to very large, the properties of the waves change and make different uses possible. The different parts of the spectrum are given different names although they really blend one into the next without a sudden change. Some X-rays and gamma rays for example would be identical except for the way in which they are produced. All of the waves travel at the same speed in a vacuum and all are made from vibrating electric and magnetic fields.

The German-born scientist Albert Einstein said that waves come in small packets called photons and, in some ways, behave like particles.

? Things to do

1   A radio wave has a frequency of 200 000 Hz and a wavelength of 1500 m.
    Write down the wave equation and find the speed of the wave.

2   Find out the frequency of your local FM radio station.
    The radio wave will travel at 300 000 000 m/s.
    What is the wavelength of the wave?
    (HINT: 1 MHz = 1 000 000 Hz)

3   My mobile phone uses radio waves with a frequency of 900 MHz. If the wavelength of the waves is 0.33 m, what is the speed of the waves?

4   💻 Use the Internet or computer encyclopedias to find some uses for gamma radiation and for ultraviolet radiation.

5   Which type of wave will:
    a have the greatest frequency
    b be used to transmit satellite TV signals
    c have a frequency of 89 MHz?

Getting round the dangers

X-rays can be dangerous if their use is not monitored fairly carefully. The dangers are greater where the cells are dividing more rapidly – in young children and pregnant women – and an alternative is used. Ultrasound is now widely used to avoid the problems caused by the cumulative effects of X-rays.

Ultrasound

Ultrasound is sound which has a frequency too high to be heard by humans. The frequency of sound used in hospitals varies between 1 MHz and 10 MHz. (10 MHz is 10 million hertz – 10 million vibrations per second.) An electrical signal is passed though a special crystal which vibrates at the high frequency, sending out pulses of ultrasound. The ultrasound can penetrate into the soft tissues of the body. Each time that it meets a boundary between different layers of tissue some of it is reflected. The reflections are collected and used to create a picture of the internal organs. A special 'coupling jelly' is spread on the skin so that the sound gets into the body without too much being reflected straight back.

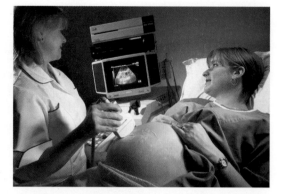

A mother can view the image of her unborn baby as the operator scans her abdomen.

One use

Ultrasound scans are often done when a woman is 16 to 20 weeks pregnant. The pictures look rather blurred but give the operator a lot of information about the baby. Usually the scanner is moved around to build up a picture from the echoes that can be seen on a monitor. The baby's heart, digestive system and limbs can be checked. It is possible to check that the baby is not suffering from spina bifida (a defect in the spine). The size of the baby's head gives a good measure of the stage of the pregnancy and when the birth can be expected.

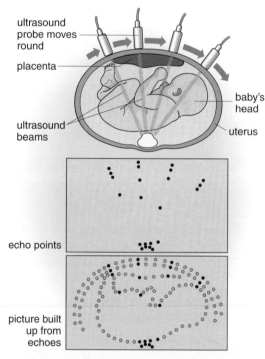

Ultrasound can be used safely on a pregnant woman, to build up a picture of her unborn baby.

Other uses

Scans are not only done during pregnancy. They are also used to look at other organs including the bladder and kidneys. The size of organs can be seen easily and checked for abnormalities, for instance harder objects, such as kidney stones, produce a strong reflection. The moving pictures also allow examination of the heart.

Ultrasound of higher frequencies will carry more energy and this can appear as heat when it is absorbed. This can be used to treat back and shoulder pains. Kidney stones can sometimes be treated by a sudden burst of ultrasound. The vibration causes the stone to break up without needing surgery.

There are non-medical uses too. Ultrasound can be used to clean delicate instruments where the dirt is vibrated loose. It can be used to find flaws in metal and to look for cracks in concrete structures.

Why so high?

The high frequency is needed to avoid the sound waves being diffracted between the organs of the body.

You will have seen in *Communicating information* (Y10) that waves spread out as they pass through a narrow gap. This is called diffraction.

Very high frequency ultrasound is now used in some specialised microscopes and even as a catalyst in some types of chemical reaction.

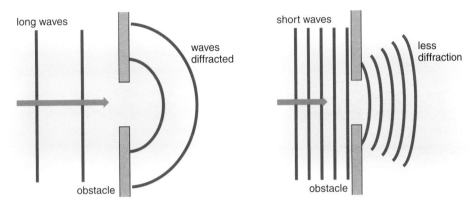

The diffraction through a gap is less as the wavelength becomes shorter.
(Remember that as the wavelength gets shorter, the frequency is higher.)

Higher frequency waves are diffracted less than lower frequency waves and can show clearer pictures of smaller objects. This is important where detail is needed.

? Things to do

1   Read the section about ultrasound and design a reassuring leaflet for mothers-to-be telling them how scans are done and why they are safe for the baby.

2   Compare the results of ultrasound scans and their safety with the use of X-rays.

3   Explain how the high frequency of ultrasound helps to get a clearer picture than lower frequencies could produce.

4   Radio waves sometimes reach their receivers by diffraction around or over hills. Which wavebands would be best for this? Draw a diagram to show how it works.
    (HINT: Look at *Communicating information*, Y10, if you are stuck!)

1 The average yearly radiation dose to a person in the UK is about 2.5 mSv. Make a list of the sources of this radiation.

2 Copy and complete the following table, filling in the missing information.

Particle	Protons	Neutrons	Electrons	Symbol
Most common type of carbon atom	6	6		
Radioactive carbon atom		8	6	14 C
Chlorine atom	17			35 Cl
_____ atom	92	143		
Sodium atom	11	12	11	

Complete the following sentences:

The two atoms of carbon in the table are _____ of carbon. The have the same number of _____ and _____ so their chemistry is the same but they have a different number of _____.

3 Emma's mum fell and went to the hospital to have her arm examined.

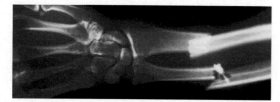

The doctor asked how many X-rays she had had recently. He then asked if she was pregnant before he sent her for an X-ray.

a Why did he do this? Explain what effect X-rays might have on the cells.

b Why should you try to avoid having too many X-rays?

c What do you think the radiographer will do to avoid getting a dangerous dose?

d The picture shows the X-ray of her arm. Why do the bones show as white when the muscles are grey?

4 Joanne has been sent to the hospital by her doctor for an ultrasound scan on her kidneys.

a Explain briefly to her what ultrasound is and how it works.

b The sound used has a very short wavelength. Explain why this is important in getting as much detail as possible in the picture.

5 Chloe is a history student. She is trying to find out the age of a wooden boat that has been buried in mud for a very long time. A friend suggests it could be dated by measuring the carbon-14 in it.
Her reference book says that carbon-14 is a beta emitter with a half-life of 5570 years.

a Write a decay equation for the emission of a beta particle from an atom of carbon-14.

b What is meant by half-life?

When the wood was growing it would exchange carbon with its surroundings so that the proportion of carbon-14 stays constant.

c What happens to the amount of carbon-14 after the tree is cut down?

d If the proportion of carbon-14 is only one quarter of that in a tree that is growing now, what is the approximate age of the boat? What assumptions are being made when Chloe works this out?

6 Ultrasound can be used to measure the distance to an object. The machine sends out a pulse of ultrasound and then measures the time for an echo to return. The distance is then worked out and displayed on a small LCD screen. The speed of ultrasound in the air is 340 m/s. The echo returns in 0.012 s. How far away is the object?

INTRODUCING
Controlling change

Try these first

1 What is the normal temperature of a healthy human body?

   a 0 °C b 25 °C c 37 °C d 98 °C

2 Which of these foods is eaten mainly as a source of energy?

   a meat b fish c bread d eggs

3 Which two raw materials do plants use for making food?

4 Which part of a plant does water enter through?

5 Which gas does a plant release into the air as a result of photosynthesis?

6 Why is smoking bad for your health?

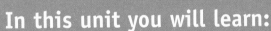
The baby shows a response to the stimulus from the toddler.

This plant shows phototropic growth in response to the light from one side.

In this unit you will learn:

- how and why humans maintain a constant internal environment
- how factors such as tiredness and drugs can affect us
- how size affects temperature control in animals
- how plants absorb and transport water
- how plants transport the products of photosynthesis
- how information and instructions are carried round the body by nerves
- how hormones work
- how plant hormones control the growth of plants.

You can find human beings in most areas of our planet, from the coldest to the hottest regions. However, all of these people have a body temperature of 37 °C, no matter where they live.

Temperature is not the only thing that is kept constant in our bodies. The levels of glucose and water in our blood are also kept constant. The process of keeping everything in our bodies at a constant level is called **homeostasis** and is usually referred to as 'keeping a constant internal environment'. Life depends on a delicate balance of chemical reactions, controlled by enzymes. Enzymes are very sensitive to changes in temperature. If your temperature changes by just a few degrees, reactions get out of balance and you start to feel ill. Your body has many mechanisms to keep your temperature at 37 °C.

Before birth, a baby is surrounded by water, and by almost constant temperature. After birth, it is surrounded by air, and the temperature varies. Babies, especially premature babies, find it hard to cope with changes in temperature and must be protected from too much heat or cold.

Temperature control is a very complicated business. Not only does the temperature around you vary, but the reactions inside you generate heat energy.

Unless you can lose energy into your surroundings at a rate which just balances this, you cannot control your temperature. However big or small an animal is, temperature control is still a problem.

No matter where you live, you have a body temperature of 37 °C.

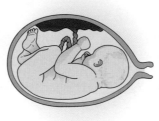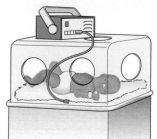

Babies are protected from temperature changes in the womb and sometimes need help, especially if they are born prematurely.

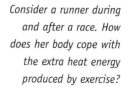

Consider a runner during and after a race. How does her body cope with the extra heat energy produced by exercise?

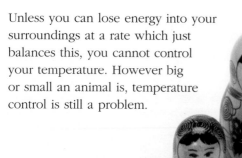

Is big better?

Some small animals, such as mice, have difficulty in keeping their body temperature warm enough. Large animals, like elephants, have difficulty keeping cool enough.

The chemical processes inside the bodies of animals generate heat energy. Because of the larger scale, big animals have to lose more heat than small animals to keep their temperature steady. However, larger animals also have a bigger surface area of skin through which the heat can escape!

To see how these two factors might affect cooling for animals of different sizes, look at these pictures of cubes of different sizes.

Can you see any feature on these elephants which is adapted to help them keep cool?

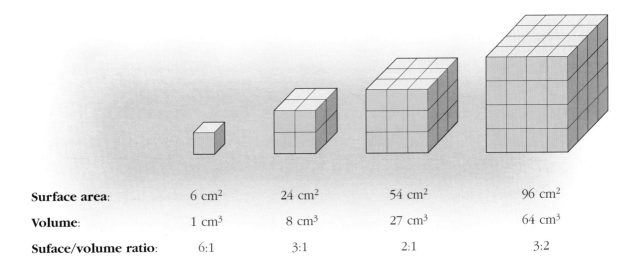

Surface area:	6 cm²	24 cm²	54 cm²	96 cm²
Volume:	1 cm³	8 cm³	27 cm³	64 cm³
Suface/volume ratio:	6:1	3:1	2:1	3:2

Surface area increases as animals get bigger, but body volume increases even faster. In hot weather, bigger animals find it harder to keep cool. In cold weather, it is the other way round – the body temperature of a small animal is likely to fall faster.

Things to do

You can try out this size effect for yourself. Use different sized beakers containing different amounts of hot water to represent different sized animals.

For best results, stand the beaker on an insulating surface (such as a ceiling tile) and cover the top with an insulating lid.

1   Describe the processes by which heat energy is carried away from the beakers.

2   Why is it important to put lids on the beakers during these experiments?

2 How animals control their temperature

Warm-blooded or cold-blooded? CC1, CC2

Animals that keep their internal body temperature the same at all times are called **endotherms.** Like us, they are warm-blooded, and have a range of automatic mechanisms (such as shivering) to help control their temperature.

Other animals have body temperatures which are not so well controlled and change with the surroundings. They are said to be cold-blooded (**ectotherms**). Cold-blooded animals have to rely on behavioural adaptations to control their temperature (for example, sheltering from the hot Sun to keep cool, or basking in the Sun to get warm).

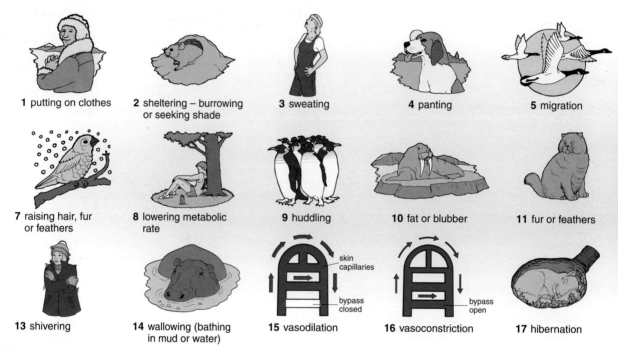

1 putting on clothes

2 sheltering – burrowing or seeking shade

3 sweating

4 panting

5 migration

7 raising hair, fur or feathers

8 lowering metabolic rate

9 huddling

10 fat or blubber

11 fur or feathers

13 shivering

14 wallowing (bathing in mud or water)

15 vasodilation

16 vasoconstriction

17 hibernation

These pictures show some of the adaptations used by animals to help control their temperatures.

? Things to do

1   Work with a small group to discuss all of these pictures of adaptations.

2   For each one, decide whether it is an automatic mechanism or a behavioural one, and whether it helps to keep the animal warm or cool.

3   Your teacher may give you (or ask you to find out) more information, which you can match to each of the pictures to help explain how each adaptation works.

4   Look at the photograph of elephants on page 25. The very large ears provide a large extra area of skin which helps the elephants keep cool. See if you can find any other examples of this type of adaptation.

5   Explain why the baby elephant will find it harder to keep warm in cold weather than the mother does.

The structure of human skin

As you learnt in *Keeping healthy* (Y10), your skin provides protection against infection. However, skin does much more than this. The various structures in the skin are adapted to help you control heat loss in order to keep a constant body temperature.

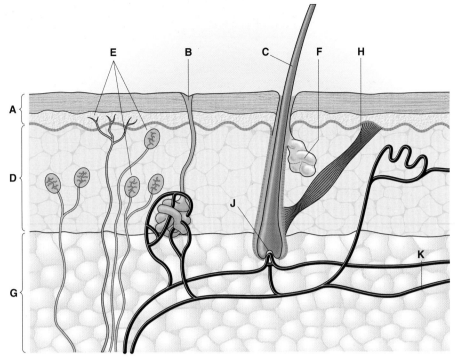

A cross-section of human skin showing the different parts.

6 lowering hair, fur or feathers

12 increasing metabolic rate

18 basking

Skin is made up of three layers:

- **The epidermis** (A). Cells in the epidermis divide to replace those on the surface as they are worn away.
- **The dermis** (D). This is the layer which contains nerve endings and most of the temperature control structures.
- **Subcutaneous fat** (G). This layer of fat cells provides insulation and also protects against damage if you bump into things!

Things to do

6 Match each of the words in this list to one of the labels on the diagram of the skin:

    sweat gland   sweat pore   nerve cell   hair   oil gland   hair muscle
    hair root   blood vessel

7 Search in biology or medical books to find out the function of each of these structures.

8 List which ones: **a** can help you to lose heat faster

                    b can slow down heat loss

                    c can work in either of these ways.

In order to react properly to changes around you, you need to be able to **sense** what is happening. Humans have five senses: hearing, sight, smell, taste and touch. You can detect what is happening around you because certain parts of your body have **receptors** that are sensitive to external conditions. Think about which parts of your body are involved in each of the five senses.

With a large organism like a human, it is vital to have systems for passing information round the body. It would be no use being able to see danger coming if you couldn't pass messages to your muscles to move away. Animals have two systems for information and control: the nervous system and the hormone system.

Nerves for rapid responses (SS) CC3, CC4

Nerves are a bit like a telephone system. They pass messages (**impulses**) quickly from place to place. The top diagram shows how the nervous system reaches every part of the body. The lower diagram shows some of the different types of highly specialised cells that make up the system.

Neurons are long, thin cells which carry nerve impulses (like the wires in a telephone system).

Receptor cells (some are shown in the diagram of the skin on page 27) send tiny electrical impulses through **sensory neurons**, most of which go to the spinal cord, where **relay neurons**, or **intermediate neurons**, carry the nerve impulses on to the brain. The brain analyses the signals and decides what action to take. Impulses are then sent back along **motor neurons** to control the muscles.

To make the system work, nerve signals have to pass from one neuron to another. Junctions between neurons are called **synapses**. When an electrical signal reaches the end of a neuron, a chemical similar to adrenaline is released. This chemical triggers a new electrical signal in the next neuron, so that the message passes on. The chemical is quickly broken down, so that the system is ready for the next message.

Some drugs interfere with either the production or the removal of the chemical signal, and so they interfere with the working of the nervous system.

The nervous system reaches all parts of the body.

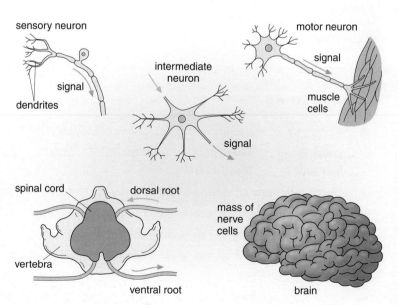

The nervous system comprises many specialised components.

Responding to emergencies

Perhaps you have measured your reaction time – how long it takes for you to react to a stimulus. On average this is about a third of a second. Sometimes you need to react as fast as possible. Reflex reactions help you to do this.

Your ears, eyes, nose, tongue and skin are sense organs. Messages from them pass through sensory neurons to relay neurons in the spinal cord. These relay neurons pass signals on to two different places.

Reflex responses

Some reactions, such as dropping something hot, need to happen very quickly to save you from injury. Neurons in the spinal cord can relay signals directly through motor neurons to give an immediate reaction, without waiting for the signal to reach the brain and be processed.

Reactions like this are called **reflex actions** and happen automatically, without thought. The shortened route for the signals is called a **reflex arc**.

Conscious responses

 CC5

Neurons in the spinal cord can also pass on signals to the brain. You become aware of what is happening and can think what to do next. Often you would continue with the reflex action, but sometimes you decide to over-rule it.

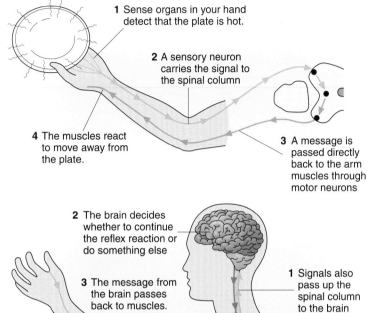

1 Sense organs in your hand detect that the plate is hot.

2 A sensory neuron carries the signal to the spinal column

3 A message is passed directly back to the arm muscles through motor neurons

4 The muscles react to move away from the plate.

2 The brain decides whether to continue the reflex reaction or do something else

3 The message from the brain passes back to muscles.

muscle

1 Signals also pass up the spinal column to the brain

motor neuron

You control many of your actions but reflex actions happen without conscious thought.

Conditioned reflexes

Saliva helps to digest food. Sometimes your salivary glands begin to work as soon as you see or smell food. This is a reflex reaction – you do not have to think about it.

A Russian scientist called Ivan Petrovich Pavlov (1849–1936) worked with dogs. He gave a sound signal every time he was about to give the dogs some food. After a while, he found that the dogs' saliva glands began to work as soon as they heard the sound, even when no food was there. The reflex reaction had been conditioned, or trained, to work in response to a new signal.

Things to do

1 Sit cross-legged. Gently tap the front of your knee just below the knee cap. What happens?

2 Stand near to a window and look at your reflection in a mirror. Now hold a book or other object so that it reduces the amount of light reaching your eye. What happens to the size of your pupils?

4 Hormones to all parts of the body

A slower system of control (SS) CC7, CC8

The nervous system is not the only control system for your body. Special organs called glands make chemicals called **hormones**, which are released into the blood. The blood carries hormones to all parts of the body, where they cause or control a range of reactions.

If the nervous system is like a telephone system – carrying rapid messages to particular places – then the **endocrine system** (or hormone system) is like a newspaper; messages travel more slowly, but reach all parts of the body.

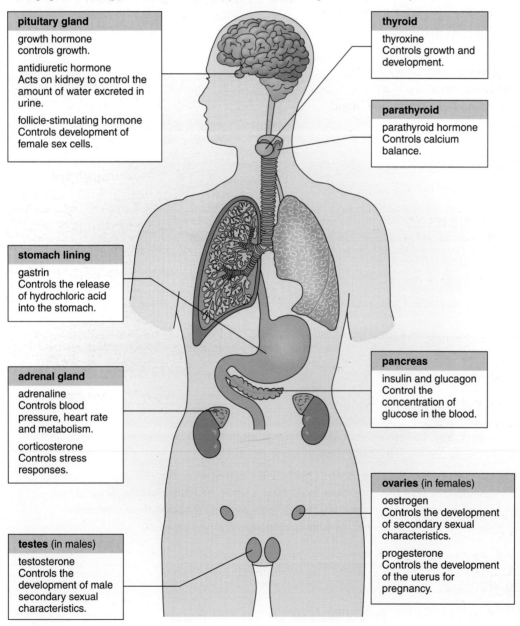

pituitary gland

growth hormone
controls growth.

antidiuretic hormone
Acts on kidney to control the
amount of water excreted in
urine.

follicle-stimulating hormone
Controls development of
female sex cells.

thyroid

thyroxine
Controls growth and
development.

parathyroid

parathyroid hormone
Controls calcium
balance.

stomach lining

gastrin
Controls the release
of hydrochloric acid
into the stomach.

pancreas

insulin and glucagon
Control the
concentration of
glucose in the blood.

adrenal gland

adrenaline
Controls blood
pressure, heart rate
and metabolism.

corticosterone
Controls stress
responses.

ovaries (in females)

oestrogen
Controls the development
of secondary sexual
characteristics.

progesterone
Controls the development
of the uterus for
pregnancy.

testes (in males)

testosterone
Controls the
development of male
secondary sexual
characteristics.

The endocrine system showing where some of your endocrine glands are, the hormones they make and the effect these have on your body.

Fight or flight – the story of adrenaline

When you are faced with danger, there is a need to be ready for emergency action.

Whether you stand and face the danger, or run away, extra strength and speed may be needed.

The signal to prepare for action must reach all parts of the body, so it is transmitted by a hormone – **adrenaline**.

Preparing for emergencies

Messages from the nervous system are sent through motor neurons to two small glands called the **adrenal** glands, found at the top of your kidneys.

In response to *emergency* signals, the adrenal glands secrete the hormone adrenaline. Adrenaline is carried to all parts of your body in the blood stream. Many organs respond.

Responding to signals

Changes in the body caused by adrenaline:

- the brain becomes more active
- the pupils of the eyes dilate (get larger)
- the heart beats faster
- blood vessels in the skin, gut and kidney become narrower
- blood pressure rises
- blood vessels in the muscles dilate
- air passages in the lungs open wider
- the basal metabolic rate increases
- glycogen is broken down to form glucose
- fat is broken down to release energy.

Sometimes fighting pays dividends ... this gazelle is chasing a predator – a jackal.

Will the predator turn into the prey? The snake fights back against the hawk.

? Things to do

1 Explain why people who are frightened often seem to have staring eyes and pale skin.

2 For each of the changes caused by adrenaline, write short notes to explain how the change would help you to respond faster and more effectively to danger.

As you grow up, some of the changes you go through are gradual (for example, you get taller). Some are more sudden (for example, girls begin to have periods, boys' voices break).

Growth

The **pituitary** gland at the underside of the brain produces a hormone called **growth hormone** which stimulates growth. The **thyroid** gland in the throat produces a hormone called **thyroxine**, which controls growth and development. The efficient working of this gland depends on iodine in your diet.

Maturation (puberty)

At a certain stage in growth, hormonal changes in the body begin changes which prepare the body for adult life. The age at which this happens can vary a lot. In boys, the **testes** produce a hormone called **testosterone**. It produces 'secondary sexual characteristics' such as facial hair and lowering of the voice.

In girls, the **ovaries** begin to secrete **oestrogen**. This controls the development of breasts and the beginning of periods. The ovaries also produce another hormone, **progesterone**. It acts on the **uterus** (womb) to prepare it for pregnancy and on the breasts to prepare them for breast feeding.

Hormones and the menstrual cycle

 CC9

From the time of puberty onwards, most women experience the menstrual cycle approximately once every 28 days. The walls of the uterus are built up with a lining ready to receive an egg from the ovaries. In most months the egg is not fertilised and the lining round the walls of the uterus breaks down and the cycle begins all over again.

The progress of the cycle every month is controlled by hormones. Three hormones, oestrogen, progesterone and **follicle-stimulating hormone (FSH)** interact to control the different stages of the cycle.

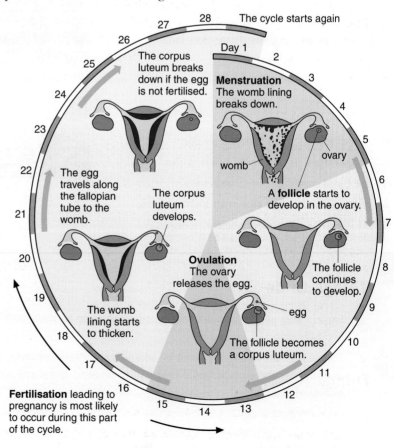

In most women, the menstrual cycle lasts approximately 28 days.

Hormone control of the menstrual cycle

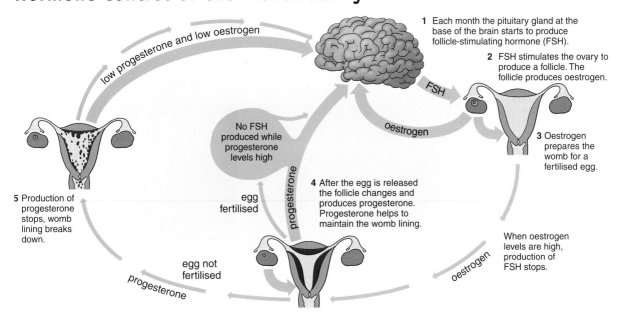

1 Each month the pituitary gland at the base of the brain starts to produce follicle-stimulating hormone (FSH).

2 FSH stimulates the ovary to produce a follicle. The follicle produces oestrogen.

3 Oestrogen prepares the womb for a fertilised egg.

When oestrogen levels are high, production of FSH stops.

4 After the egg is released the follicle changes and produces progesterone. Progesterone helps to maintain the womb lining.

No FSH produced while progesterone levels high

5 Production of progesterone stops, womb lining breaks down.

low progesterone and low oestrogen

FSH

oestrogen

progesterone

egg fertilised

egg not fertilised

progesterone

The menstrual cycle starts with production of FSH in the pituitary gland.

Look at the picture above. Start at the pituitary gland and follow the arrows to see how the hormones interact:

- if the woman is not pregnant, oestrogen and progesterone levels are low at the end of the cycle, and this stimulates production of FSH to begin the next cycle.
- if the woman is pregnant, levels of progesterone will be higher. No FSH is produced, no more eggs are released, and the lining of the womb does not break down, but remains to protect the developing embryo.
- FSH is only produced when levels of both oestrogen and progesterone are low.

The contraceptive pill

Scientists have used knowledge about hormones to develop the contraceptive pill. The pill contains synthetic hormones, which have similar effects on the body to oestrogen and progesterone. The level of hormones in the pill stops the pituitary gland from producing FSH, so the ovaries do not produce any eggs. If no egg is released, the woman cannot become pregnant, although she will still have a period every month.

The pill is also given to help women who have irregular cycles. The hormones control the cycle so that periods become more regular.

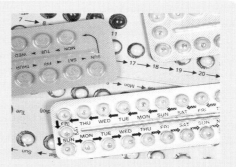

The contraceptive pill comes in packs which last one cycle. Each pill is placed in a section marked with the day of the week on which it should be taken.

Things to do

1 Write notes to explain how taking contraceptive pills can prevent pregnancy.

2 Look at medical leaflets to find the advantages and disadvantages associated with taking the contraceptive pill.

6 Keeping blood sugar under control

The main source of energy for body processes is a sugar called glucose. Glucose is very soluble and is carried round the body in the blood. Energy is released by reaction of glucose with dissolved oxygen to form carbon dioxide and water.

Glucose + oxygen →   carbon dioxide + water

$$C_6H_{12}O_6 \;+\; 6O_2 \;\rightarrow\; 6CO_2 \;+\; 6H_2O$$

This process is called cellular **respiration** and takes place in body cells. Glucose is being used up all of the time to provide the energy your body needs.

As you digest food, or sugary drinks, extra glucose enters your blood. So, the level of glucose in the blood varies from time to time. However, your body needs a constant, steady level of glucose. This level is kept in balance by two hormones working together. This is another example of **homeostasis**. Both of these hormones are made in the pancreas.

● **Insulin**: (reduces glucose levels in the blood)
Insulin removes glucose from the blood by turning it into insoluble glycogen which is stored in the liver. If the level of glucose in the blood is too high, more insulin is produced, and glucose is removed and stored in the liver.

● **Glucagon**: (increases glucose levels in the blood)
If the level of glucose in blood falls below normal, extra glucagon is produced. Glucagon breaks down glycogen in the liver, releasing more glucose into the blood.

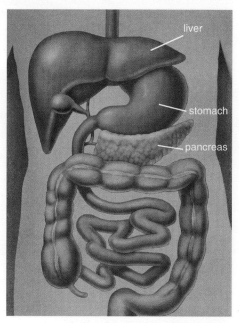

A computer-generated image showing the location of the human stomach, liver and pancreas.

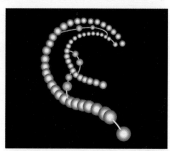

A computer-generated image of the molecular structure of insulin.

Steady levels of blood sugar (SS) CC10

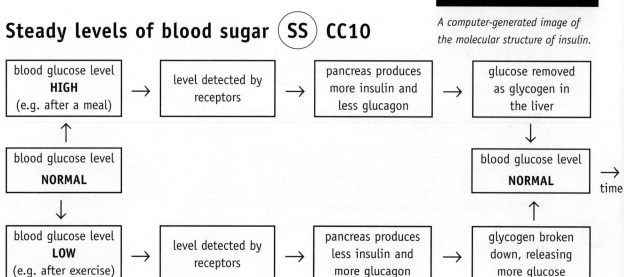

Diabetes – sugar out of balance

It is estimated that there are 2 million people in Britain who suffer from diabetes. This is a metabolic disorder in which the sufferer loses the ability to control sugar levels in the blood. Symptoms include feeling very tired, blurred vision, increased thirst, and passing large amounts of urine.

Type I diabetes

Type I diabetes often develops early in life. The pancreas stops producing any insulin at all.

Without insulin, glucose cannot be absorbed and used by body cells. People who suffer from type I diabetes need to take insulin regularly. Insulin can only be given by injection: it is a protein, and if taken by mouth the digestive system would break it down.

Type II diabetes

Type II diabetes often develops later in life. The pancreas is still making insulin, but either there is not enough, or it isn't working properly.

Both types of diabetes require very careful control of diet. In both types, it is important for the patient to regularly check their blood sugar levels to make sure that they are not too high or too low. Several types of test kit are available, all require a tiny drop of blood to be tested.

People with diabetes carry a card like this.

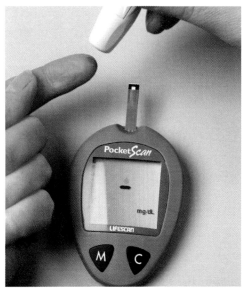

A pinprick on the finger will provide enough sample for a blood test.

? Things to do

1. Make a list of the hormones mentioned on the last four pages. For each one, say where in the body it is produced, and what actions it causes.

2. Explain why it is necessary to have **two** hormones to control the level of sugar in the blood.

3. Explain why diabetics should have small, regular meals, at frequent intervals.

4. Suggest what a diabetic should do if they accidentally injected themselves with too much insulin.

5. Discuss the problems a diabetic person might face if they wished to take part in a marathon run.

Unlike animals, plants do not have nerves, but they do make hormones, which can be passed from one part of the plant to another in the sap. Responses caused by plant hormones are slow, so to see the effects it is necessary to observe plants for some time.

Effects on plant growth in response to outside influences are called **tropisms**.

Plants can respond to outside influences, such as light or gravity by growing towards the influence (**positive tropism**) or away from it (**negative tropism**). One important group of plant hormones, called **auxins**, control plant growth.

This plant is growing towards the light.

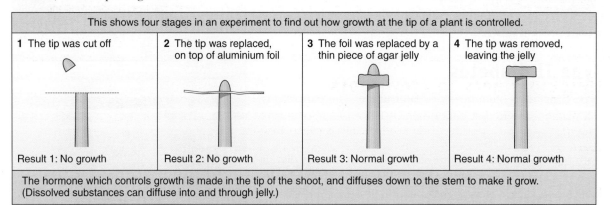

This shows four stages in an experiment to find out how growth at the tip of a plant is controlled.

1 The tip was cut off	2 The tip was replaced, on top of aluminium foil	3 The foil was replaced by a thin piece of agar jelly	4 The tip was removed, leaving the jelly
Result 1: No growth	Result 2: No growth	Result 3: Normal growth	Result 4: Normal growth

The hormone which controls growth is made in the tip of the shoot, and diffuses down to the stem to make it grow. (Dissolved substances can diffuse into and through jelly.)

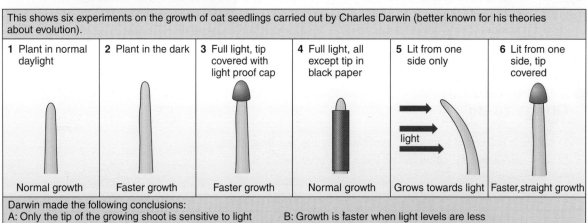

This shows six experiments on the growth of oat seedlings carried out by Charles Darwin (better known for his theories about evolution).

1 Plant in normal daylight	2 Plant in the dark	3 Full light, tip covered with light proof cap	4 Full light, all except tip in black paper	5 Lit from one side only	6 Lit from one side, tip covered
Normal growth	Faster growth	Faster growth	Normal growth	Grows towards light	Faster, straight growth

Darwin made the following conclusions:
A: Only the tip of the growing shoot is sensitive to light   B: Growth is faster when light levels are less
C: When the plant is lit from one side, growth is fastest on the unlit side, which pushes the stem towards the light.

The tendency of plants to grow towards the light is called **phototropism** (it is a positive response, because the plant grows towards the stimulus). A great deal of work is still going on to try to explain these results, but scientists are still not certain how uneven lighting affects the movement of the growth hormones.

? Things to do

1   Which of the 10 results help to explain each of the conclusions A, B and C?

Geotropism

When you plant seeds, you often just scatter them – it doesn't seem to matter which way up they go. How do the stems and roots of plants know which way to grow?

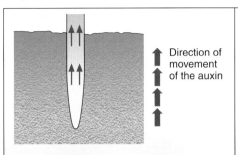 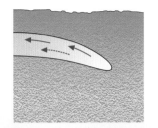 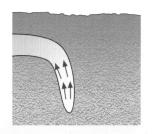

When placed vertically, a root grows straight down. Auxin produced in the tip spreads upwards across the whole width of root, giving even growth.	When placed at an angle, growth is fastest on the upper surface of the root, pushing the tip downwards as it grows.	As with phototropism, scientists are still trying to identify all the factors which affect this behaviour. Plants know what they are doing, but we can't explain it yet!

Direction of movement of the auxin

Helping plants to grow roots

Some of the auxins made in plants promote the growth of roots. One of these which can be made synthetically is called **indole acetic acid (IAA)**. IAA is very useful to market gardeners and other plant growers.

One way to make new plants is to take cuttings.

Small pieces, including some leaves, are cut from a plant. If the small pieces are planted and watered, they can grow into complete new plants.

This is one way to be certain of getting new plants which are clones of the original – they have the same genes, so will show all of the same characteristics.

Unfortunately, the cuttings sometimes do not form new roots, so they die. If the cutting is dipped into a dilute solution of IAA before planting, the auxin helps new roots to form, so the cutting is more likely to grow successfully.

1

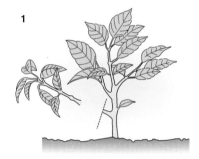

2

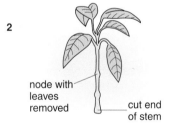

node with leaves removed — cut end of stem

3

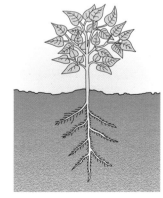

A plant may be grown from a cutting. It can be encouraged to grow roots by using auxins.

? Things to do

2   Find out the meaning of the word **haptotropism**, and find pictures of some plants which show this particular type of tropism. Explain why it is useful to the plants.

3   Design a leaflet which a garden centre can give to customers to explain to them how to take and grow cuttings from their plants.

In dry weather, plants soon wilt - they become limp and floppy. If house plants are not watered, they soon die.

Water enters plants from the soil, through tiny hairs on the plant roots. The process is called **osmosis**.

What is osmosis?

Molecules (particles) are always moving. If someone near you is wearing perfume, or making coffee, you soon notice the smell. Tiny particles of coffee or perfume spread out through the air. This spreading-by-moving is called **diffusion**. Diffusion can happen in liquids too – the colour and flavour from a tea bag soon spreads through hot water.

Osmosis is a special kind of diffusion. It happens when two solutions are separated by a semi-permeable membrane, which will let water molecules pass through, but not molecules of the dissolved substances.

The membrane of plant root hair cells is semi-permeable. The top diagram shows how particles are arranged when water is separated from a solution by a semi-permeable membrane.

On the left (water) side, water molecules are closer together. On the right, some of the spaces next to the membrane are blocked by solute molecules. Water passes both ways, but on balance, more passes from left to right. This net movement of water is called osmosis. It will continue until the concentration is the same on both sides, or until pressure builds up to stop it.

Plant root hairs have a large surface area. Water from the soil is drawn into the solution inside. Plant nutrients also pass into the hairs.

You can see other examples of osmosis. Sultanas are made by drying grapes in sunlight. If sultanas are soaked in water, they swell up as water passes in through the cell membrane.

pure water — solution

In osmosis water passes across a semi-permeable membrane until concentrations of the solutions either side of the membrane are the same.

The heat from sunlight evaporates the water from these grapes.

Moving water up through the plant

Once the water reaches the centre of the root, it travels up the stem through a system of hollow tubes. These are the remains of dead cells, with their ends removed. They look rather like very small straws. They are called **xylem** vessels.

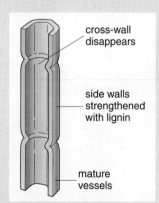

cross-wall disappears

side walls strengthened with lignin

mature vessels

A xylem vessel from a plant stem.

The transpiration stream

The roots, the xylem vessels in the stem and branches, and the leaves of a plant are all involved in movement of water.

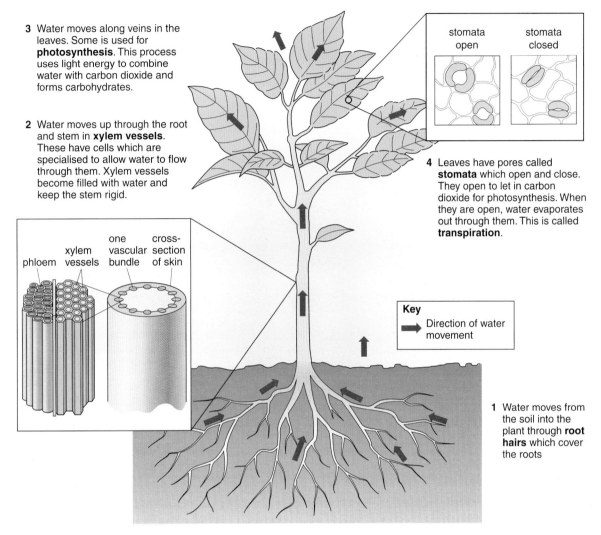

3 Water moves along veins in the leaves. Some is used for **photosynthesis**. This process uses light energy to combine water with carbon dioxide and forms carbohydrates.

2 Water moves up through the root and stem in **xylem vessels**. These have cells which are specialised to allow water to flow through them. Xylem vessels become filled with water and keep the stem rigid.

phloem   xylem vessels   one vascular bundle   cross-section of skin

stomata open   stomata closed

4 Leaves have pores called **stomata** which open and close. They open to let in carbon dioxide for photosynthesis. When they are open, water evaporates out through them. This is called **transpiration**.

Key
→ Direction of water movement

1 Water moves from the soil into the plant through **root hairs** which cover the roots

The movement of water through the plant makes up the transpiration stream.

? Things to do

1   Look carefully at the way the xylem vessels are arranged in the stem. Explain why plants wilt (become limp and floppy) in dry weather.

2   When the plant is short of water, the stomata on the leaves close.

   a   Explain why this helps the plant to survive in dry periods.

   b   Suggest how this will affect the rate of photosynthesis in the plant.

   c   Irrigation (supplying water to crops) is expensive. Explain why it is profitable for farmers to irrigate crops in dry weather.

9 Water to all parts

Push or pull?

What sort of forces make water move up through a plant?

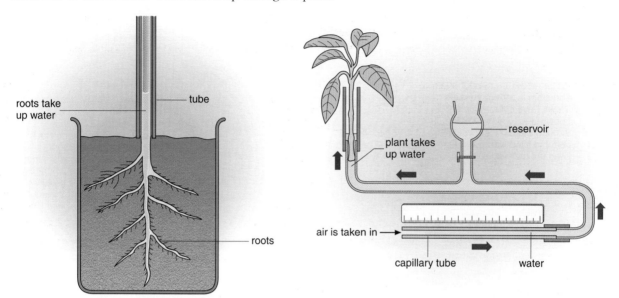

The roots of a cut plant are placed in a beaker.

The stem and leaves of the cut plant are attached to a reservoir of water.

A plant was cut across the stem, just above the roots, and the two parts were set up as shown in the pictures. The water rose just a little way above the root in the left hand picture, then stopped. A force called root pressure can lift water a little way, but not all the way up a tall plant.

In the right hand picture, water moved up through the plant and the movement could be seen as more and more air was drawn into the capillary tube. It seems that there is some force which 'pulls' water up a plant!

Water has two properties which allow it to be pulled up like this:

- **adhesion**: water molecules are attracted to many other types of molecules – this is why water clings to surfaces
- **cohesion**: water molecules are attracted to other water molecules, and stick together – this is why water often forms small round drops on a surface instead of a thin flat layer.

?

Things to do

1   Take two microscope slides. Place a single drop of water on one of them, then put the other slide on top. Now try to pull the two slides apart.

Where does the 'pull' come from? (SS) CC17, CC18

Look at the figure of a cross-section through a leaf. Notice the opening in the lower surface. These openings are called **stomata**. Some of the water which is carried up to the leaf is used in **photosynthesis**. The rest **evaporates** through the stomata. The energy of sunlight makes the water evaporate and so provides the driving force to keep water moving up the plant.

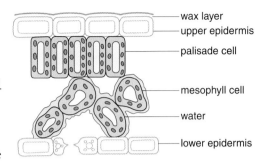

A cross-section of a leaf to show the layers of cells.

wax layer
upper epidermis
palisade cell
mesophyll cell
water
lower epidermis

Too much evaporation would be a problem for the plant. It needs to have openings in the leaf to allow carbon dioxide to enter, and oxygen to escape – but it does not want to lose too much water. Cells on either side of the stomata (called **guard cells**) help to control evaporation.

When water is plentiful the guard cells become turgid (full of water) and push apart, increasing the opening. When water supplies are limited, the guard cells become flaccid (limp) and sag together, closing the opening and reducing evaporation. Of course, this also reduces gas exchange and so slows down photosynthesis. This partly explains why plants don't grow so well in dry weather.

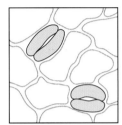

The lower surface of a leaf has stomata (open on the left and closed on the right) to allow passage of gases and water.

Transport up and down

Photosynthesis happens in the leaves, but the substances which are made are needed in all parts of the plant. Sugars and other dissolved substances are carried down from the leaves through phloem tissue.

Phloem is made up of long, thin cells. The cells join end to end and the joining cross walls have lots of tiny holes. For this reason, the phloem cells are called sieve tubes. The movement of dissolved sugars and other substances up and down the plant is called translocation.

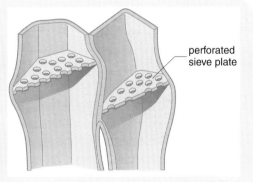

perforated sieve plate

The structure of phloem showing the 'sieve-like' cross walls.

? Things to do

2 Draw a diagram of a complete plant and label it to show:

root hairs **vascular bundles**
stomata **guard cells**

3 Write short notes to explain how all of these tissues work together to control movement of water through the plant.

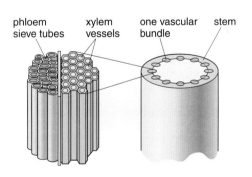

phloem sieve tubes xylem vessels one vascular bundle stem

Phloem and xylem tissues are found together in stems, arranged in long strands called vascular bundles.

1 Imagine you have to stand outside and wait for a bus on a cold winter day.

   a Describe automatic responses to cold and how they work.

   b Describe things you could choose to do which would help to protect you from the cold.

2 Make a table to show which sense organs detect each of these things? (Some may be detected by more than one sense).

   a a red traffic light

   b smoke from a wood fire

   c whether there is sugar in a cup of tea

   d a hot plate

   e the bell for the end of the lesson

3 Each of the following is a part of the nervous system:

   A brain   B sensory neuron

   C spinal cord   D motor neuron

   Which of the parts above:

   a carries signals to muscles

   b is involved in learning

   c is not involved in reflex actions?

4 Write brief notes about the differences in the way the nervous system acts, compared to the hormone system.

5 Arrange the following statements into order to show what happens after you eat a sweet sticky bun:

   A the blood sugar level starts to decrease

   B insulin circulates in the blood

   C sugar circulating in the blood reaches the pancreas

   D insulin encourages cells to take up sugar

   E cells in the pancreas release insulin

   F the blood sugar level rises

6 New plants can sometimes be grown from 'cuttings'. Explain what can be done to help the cuttings to grow.

7 The roots of plants are often covered with fine hairs. What are the hairs for?

8 Describe a series of experiments you could carry out to find the concentration of dissolved substances in the cells of a potato. Explain how you would use your results.

9 Plants can grow in response to external stimuli. In each of the following cases, say what type of tropism is shown, and whether it is positive or negative.

   a A plant on a table in the middle of a room is growing so that it leans over towards the window.

   b Some seeds were just sprinkled on the ground and covered with soil. All of them grew with the stem going upwards and the root growing down.

   c The stems of honeysuckle bushes curl round any supporting trellis.

10 This table shows the internal temperature of different animals when they are kept in surroundings at various different temperatures:

Outside temperature (°C)	Internal temperature of the animal (°C)		
	Cat	Duck-billed platypus	Lizard
10	38	32	10
15	39	32	15
20	39	33	20
25	40	33	25
30	40	34	30
35	40	37	35
40	41	40	40

Plot the results on a graph. Which animal(s) are cold-blooded?

INTRODUCING
Making use of oil

Try these first

1 Use these words to fill in the blanks (you can use words more than once).

physical   polymer   liquid

thermoplastic   gas   monomer

2 When a substance boils it changes from a _____ to a _____.

3 Condensation is when a substance changes from a _____ to a _____.

4 Both these changes are examples of a _____ change.

5 Plastics that melt when they get hot are called _____.

6 Small molecules called _____ join up to make long chain molecules called _____.

The primary distillation towers of an oil refinery.

In this unit you will learn:

- about the oil industry, starting with how oil was formed from dead sea creatures millions of years ago

- how petrol and other fuels are separated from crude oil using fractional distillation

- how crude oil products are used for fuels and chemicals

- about how finding fuels for the future is very important

- about hydrocarbon molecules in oil, called alkanes and alkenes

- how plastics and fibres are made by addition and condensation reactions

- about the advantages and disadvantages of recycling.

Oil is extracted from layers deep beneath the seabed.

1 What can we make from oil?

Oil from oil wells is called **crude oil**. It is a mixture of many compounds which can be separated by distillation. Most of the products are burned as fuels, but some are used to make many useful products.

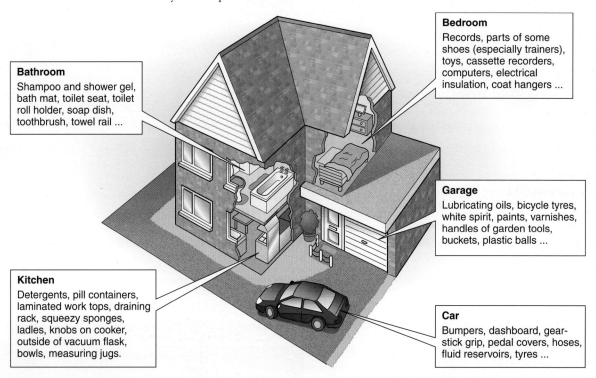

Bedroom
Records, parts of some shoes (especially trainers), toys, cassette recorders, computers, electrical insulation, coat hangers ...

Bathroom
Shampoo and shower gel, bath mat, toilet seat, toilet roll holder, soap dish, toothbrush, towel rail ...

Garage
Lubricating oils, bicycle tyres, white spirit, paints, varnishes, handles of garden tools, buckets, plastic balls ...

Kitchen
Detergents, pill containers, laminated work tops, draining rack, squeezy sponges, ladles, knobs on cooker, outside of vacuum flask, bowls, measuring jugs.

Car
Bumpers, dashboard, gear-stick grip, pedal covers, hoses, fluid reservoirs, tyres ...

Oil is not only used as fuel but as a source of compounds used in the manufacture of many useful products.

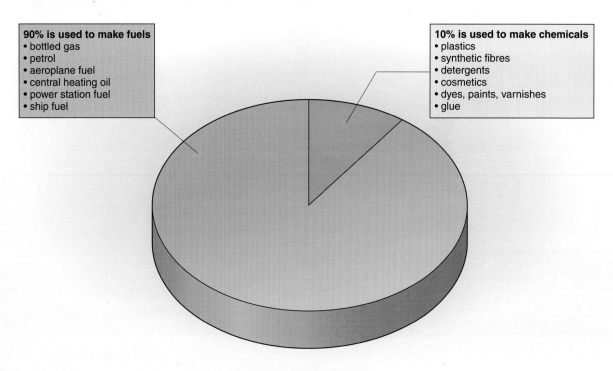

90% is used to make fuels
• bottled gas
• petrol
• aeroplane fuel
• central heating oil
• power station fuel
• ship fuel

10% is used to make chemicals
• plastics
• synthetic fibres
• detergents
• cosmetics
• dyes, paints, varnishes
• glue

What is crude oil used for?

Where does oil come from? MU1, MU2

Life began in the seas, many millions of years ago (**a**). Ever since then, the processes which form oil have been slowly taking place.

Dead plants and animals fall to the bottom of the sea and become covered with mud (**b**). The mud protects the remains from predators and keeps out oxygen.

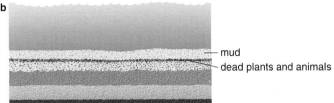

Over millions of years, pressure from layers above turns the mud into rock (**c**), and anaerobic bacteria break down the plant and animal remains into oil.

Oil may be trapped because there is an **impervious layer** above it (impervious means it does not let the oil soak through). Folds and faults in the rock layers collect oil in **oil fields** (**d**). Drilling in these places with an **oil rig** allows the oil to be brought to the surface.

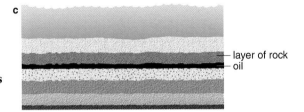

Oil is now a vital part of our economy. It is a major source of energy as well as being used to make many different materials. Oil fields are often far from the places where oil is needed most, so millions of tonnes of oil are transported round the world every year.

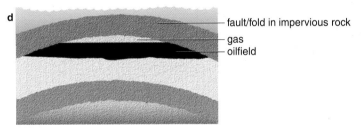

The stages in the development of an oilfield.

? Things to do

1 Write the story of a jellyfish from its life in the sea to when its molecules come to the surface on an oil rig. Use these words in your story:

   warm seas   death   mud   predators   pressure

   rock layers   oil   impervious rock   oil rig

2 Make an 'oil diary'. List all the things you use (or wear, or touch) in one hour that are made using crude oil. Organise your list into types, for example fuels, plastics, cosmetics, and so on.

3 Supposing you were asked to be in a television programme. Your challenge is to live for a day without touching or using anything from crude oil. Write down some ideas about your day that you think could be used in the programme. What frustrations do you think you would have? What funny stories could happen? Write a script for a scene that you think would make 'good viewing'.

2 Getting petrol from crude oil

Crude oil is an important raw material. It is a **mixture** of many compounds. The compounds have different **boiling points**, so they can be separated by **fractional distillation**.

Distilling oil

 MU3

The higher up the column, the lower the temperature.

Compounds with low boiling points move up the column as vapour.

As vapour rises up the column it gets further from the heaters and begins to cool.

When a compound rises to a level where the temperature is cooler than its boiling point, it condenses to liquid and collects on a tray.

Liquids with different boiling points run out at different levels.

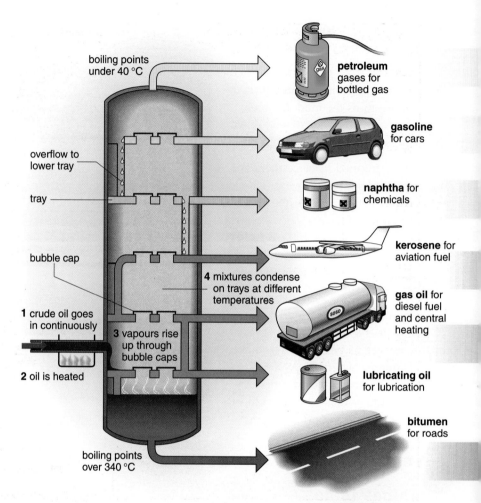

This is a fractionating column for fractional distillation, showing the main products obtained from crude oil.

Things to do

1   Write an account of what happens to a molecule of petrol in the fractionating column. Include these words in your answer:

   crude oil   mixture   heated   evaporates   condenses   fraction   petrol

2   Explain why the compounds with the lowest boiling points come out of the top of the tower.

3   The crude oil runs into the fractionating column continuously – it never needs to be emptied and filled. Make a list of reasons why using a **continuous process** saves money.

What is in the fractions? (SS) MU4

The compounds in crude oil are all **hydrocarbons**. This means that they only contain carbon and hydrogen atoms. The compounds contain different sized molecules. The bigger the molecule, the more carbon atoms it contains and the higher its **mass** and boiling point. Bigger molecules get more tangled together, and have stronger forces of attraction between them.

Fraction	Boiling range (°C)	Number of carbon atoms	Uses
petroleum gas	up to 20 °C	1–4	bottled gas
petrol (gasoline)	20–70 °C	5–10	fuels for cars
naphtha	70–120 °C	8–12	to make chemicals
paraffin (kerosene)	120–240 °C	10–16	fuel for aeroplanes
gas oil	240–350 °C	15–70	diesel, lubricants, fuel for central heating
bitumen	over 350 °C	70+	to surface roads

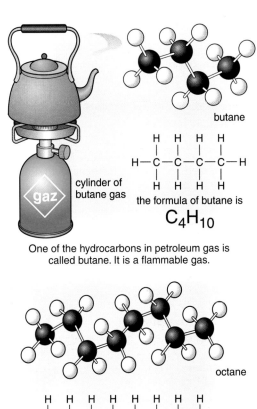

cylinder of butane gas

the formula of butane is C_4H_{10}

One of the hydrocarbons in petroleum gas is called butane. It is a flammable gas.

the formula of octane is C_8H_{18}

One of the hydrocarbons in petrol is octane. It is a liquid.

? Things to do

4 a Which fraction from crude oil has the highest boiling point?

b Which fraction from crude oil has the smallest molecules?

c Which fractions are more flammable than naphtha?

d Which fractions are more viscous than kerosene?

e Explain why a car petrol engine cannot use diesel as a fuel.

Use ideas about forces between petrol particles to explain why energy is needed to make petrol evaporate.

3 The alkane family

Almost all of the compounds in crude oil are **hydrocarbons**. They are made of just two elements, hydrogen and carbon. So many different compounds can be formed because carbon atoms are able to join to each other, forming chains which can sometimes be very long. This allows carbon to form whole families of different compounds with other elements.

The simplest family of compounds are called alkanes. They contain only carbon and hydrogen. All the chemical links in alkanes are single links. Here are some examples:

Alkane with structural formula	methane CH_4 H | H—C—H | H	ethane C_2H_6 H H | | H—C—C—H | | H H
3-D model of molecule	methane CH_4	ethane C_2H_6
Information/ properties	Methane, or natural gas, burns well. There is much more information about methane on pages 50–1.	Most crude oil has some ethane dissolved in it. It comes out as gas at the top of the fractionating column. It has many uses, including making polyethene plastic.
Alkane with structural formula	octane C_8H_{18} H H H H H H H H | | | | | | | | H—C—C—C—C—C—C—C—C—H | | | | | | | | H H H H H H H H	
3-D model of molecule	octane C_8H_{18}	
Information/ properties	Octane is a liquid that boils easily. It burns well. Petrol for cars contains octane.	
Alkane with structural formula	eicosane $C_{20}H_{42}$ H H H H H H H H H H H H H H H H H H H H | | | | | | | | | | | | | | | | | | | | H—C—C—C—C—C—C—C—C—C—C—C—C—C—C—C—C—C—C—C—C—H | | | | | | | | | | | | | | | | | | | | H H H H H H H H H H H H H H H H H H H H	
3-D model of of molecule	eicosane $C_{20}H_{42}$	
Information/ properties	Eicosane is a white, waxy solid. It is one of the compounds in paraffin wax, and is used to make candles.	

Note that all the members of the family of alkanes have names that end in **-ane**. They are called **saturated** hydrocarbons, because each available chemical link has a different atom attached to it, so no more atoms can be added on.

?

Things to do

1 Find the name and formula of the alkane which has three carbon atoms in each molecule.

Discovering properties MU5, MU6

The alkanes are a family of chemicals. Just like a real family, the alkanes are all alike in some ways, but each one is a little different to the others. Alkanes show very few chemical reactions, except that they burn. The smaller the molecules, the more easily they burn, so alkanes with small molecules are mostly used as fuels. Ones with longer chains of carbon atoms are used as lubricating oils, and the solid waxes are used in making candles, waxing food cartons and many other uses.

Working out the formula

Because there are many different alkanes, chemists have looked for a pattern that can be used to predict the chemical formula for any alkane if you know how many carbon atoms are in each molecule.

These three students (Alex, Jo and Sue) are trying to work out a pattern which they can use.

Who is right? Does more than one way work?

Jo's method can be written:

number of hydrogens = 2(n+1)

where n is the number of carbon atoms.

Write a 'general' formula like this for Sue's method.

Things to do

2   Use the method you think is best to work out the formula of an alkane with 100 carbon atoms. Would you expect this alkane to be a solid, a liquid or a gas? Explain your answer.

3   Look in chemistry books to find the names, formulas and boiling points of the first six alkanes. Plot a graph showing boiling point against number of carbon atoms. What general trend can you see?

4 Methane – friend or foe?

Where does methane come from?

Methane, CH_4, is the simplest alkane. Natural gas is mostly methane. For millions of years, bacteria have been making methane, and the process is still going on today. Many bacteria can obtain energy from food, even when there is no air available to supply oxygen. This is called **anaerobic respiration**. Anaerobic respiration by bacteria produces methane. The bacteria need a food supply, so methane is often produced where dead plants or animals are buried, in airless conditions.

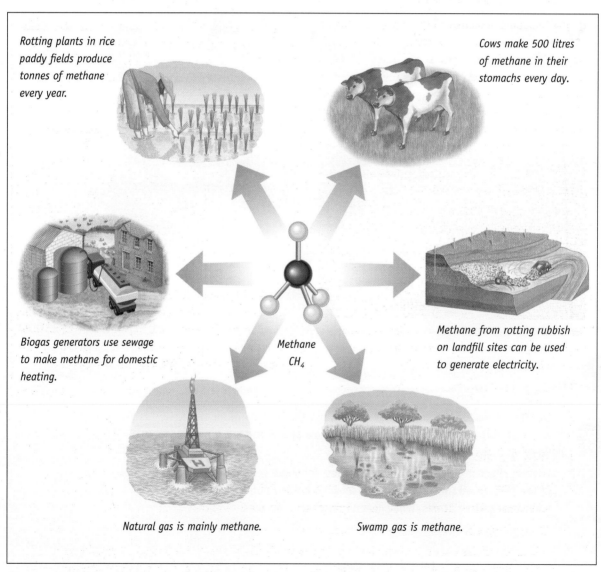

Rotting plants in rice paddy fields produce tonnes of methane every year.

Cows make 500 litres of methane in their stomachs every day.

Biogas generators use sewage to make methane for domestic heating.

Methane from rotting rubbish on landfill sites can be used to generate electricity.

Methane CH_4

Natural gas is mainly methane.

Swamp gas is methane.

Here are some of the natural sources of methane gas.

Fuel from ice!

Scientists have recently discovered vast amounts of methane trapped in ice under the oceans and in the polar ice-caps. They think there is double the amount of methane in the ice compared to the amount in all other fossil fuels left on our planet. The methane was made by bacteria living on dead plants and animals at the bottom of the sea. The methane-ice is called 'methane hydrate'. It looks exactly like normal ice, but it burns if you touch it with a lighted match! Here are two different viewpoints about methane hydrate.

MAJOR ENVIRONMENTAL THREAT!

Vast amounts of methane in ice fields throughout the world pose a serious threat to the environment. Methane causes 'global warming'. If large amounts are released into the atmosphere our climate could change, causing the ice caps to melt. Rising sea levels would put our land and cities under the sea and crops would fail.

Global warming would mean that ice under the sea could melt releasing more and more methane, sending the temperature of Earth up and up.

ENERGY PROBLEMS SOLVED!

The vast amount of methane in ice fields throughout the world could solve our 'energy crisis' by providing us with fuels long after oil and gas have run out. Geologists say it is a 'tremendous resource'.

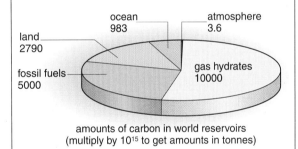

amounts of carbon in world reservoirs
(multiply by 10^{15} to get amounts in tonnes)

Geologists have successfully drilled into 'methane hydrate' 900 m below the Japanese sea. Japan has no local energy resources and hope the ice can be used as a domestic energy source. The Japanese will no longer have to buy expensive imported fuels.

? Things to do

1. 🖥 If you have use of the Internet, do searches using these words.

   methane   **landfill gas**   **biogas**   **natural gas**   **methane explosion**

   Write a 'magazine-type' article about methane.

2. 🖥 Find articles about methane hydrate (for example, search on the Internet). Highlight all points in favour of using methane hydrate as a fuel in green. Highlight all potential dangers in red. Write a short report to say whether you think scientists should disturb the methane hydrate reserves to use as fuel.

Oil in the UK

We are an 'oil producing nation' because we have our own supply of oil from the North Sea oil fields.

Crude oil is brought to refineries from the North Sea and the Middle East in huge tankers which can carry 500 000 tonnes of oil. After the oil has been refined into separate fuels it is delivered around the country in road tankers and pipelines.

Pipes are used to carry different fuels at different times, sometimes they carry petrol, sometimes diesel. There are oil terminals (where the fuels can be taken out of the pipes) throughout the country. Big oil users, such as airports like Heathrow, have their own terminal. Oil tankers collect petrol and other products from the terminals and take them to petrol stations by road.

Some of our oil supply comes from rigs in the North Sea.

35% of our oil is used for transport.

10% of our oil is used for generating electricity.

? Things to do

1   Make a list of advantages and disadvantages of moving petrol by pipeline and by oil tanker. Why do you think both methods are used?

2   Power stations and large chemical works are often built next to refineries or pipeline terminals. Explain why this makes the products cheaper and is also safer.

3   In the year 2000, lorry drivers protested about the high price of petrol by blockading oil terminals. Within days, petrol stations had no petrol and news reports were warning of supermarkets without food and of hospitals, schools and emergency services being shut down. Explain how blockading an oil terminal caused so much disruption.

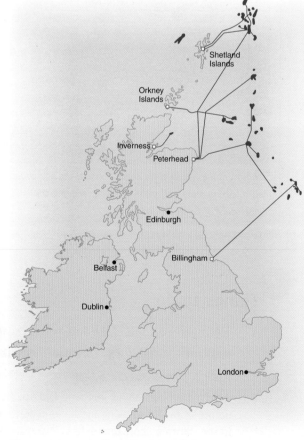

The map shows pipelines that bring oil from the North Sea to shore.

Oil around the world MU7, MU8

Crude oil from different parts of the world can vary in the amount of different fuels it contains.

Fuel	North Sea oil %	Middle East oil %
Bottled gas	2	2
Petrol	20	12
Aviation fuel	13	16
Diesel	17	20
Other (e.g. tar and ship fuels)	48	50

Things to do

4 Make a comparative bar chart to show the composition of the two types of oil.

5 Why does the UK import oil, even though we have our North Sea oil?

6 Why do you think other countries buy North Sea oil, even if they have an oil supply of their own?

How long will our oil supplies last?

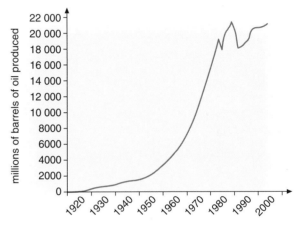

World crude oil production since 1918.

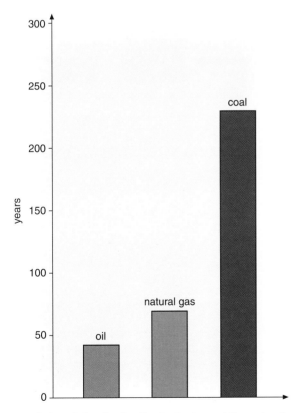

Prediction of the time it will take for the world's supply of fossil fuels to run out.

Things to do

Look at the information in the two graphs.

7 How has the amount of crude oil produced changed during the twentieth century? Make a list of reasons why you think this change has happened.

8 What will happen if we continue to use oil at our current rate? What ways are we trying to reduce how much oil we use?

9 Interview an adult about how attitudes to the use of the car have changed in their lifetime. How has this affected how much crude oil we use?

10 Write a 'save fuel' plan for your family. Why do you think people find these plans difficult to stick to?

6 Getting enough petrol

Balancing supply and demand

We have more uses for some fractions of crude oil than for others. The amount of some oil fractions is not enough to meet demand.

Look at the two charts. One shows what is in a sample of North Sea oil. The other shows our demand for the different fractions.

For which fractions is the demand greater than the supply?

For which fractions is the supply greater than demand?

In general, we need more of the smaller molecules and less of the larger ones. To make enough petrol by distillation alone, the oil refinery would have to distil more and more crude oil. The fractions which are not needed in such large quantities would have to be got rid of as waste by burning or tipping. This would make petrol cost more, waste our crude oil reserves and would be very environmentally harmful.

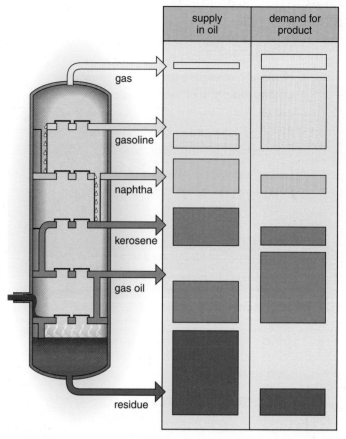

A comparison of the demand and supply of products obtained from crude oil.

Cracking the problem (SS) MU9

The larger molecules in oil can be '**cracked**', or broken up, to make smaller ones. A very **high temperature** is used (about 800 °C) and a **catalyst**. This helps by using up the larger molecules, which are not needed so much, and making more of the smaller molecules, such as octane for petrol, which are in high demand.

For example:

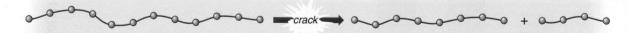

? Things to do

1   Distilling oil into fractions is a **physical** change, because the process can be easily reversed by mixing the fractions up again. No new substances are formed. Explain why cracking is a **chemical** change.

Cracking always makes at least one molecule with a **double bond**. The total numbers of carbon and hydrogen atoms must stay the same before and after cracking.

Hydrocarbons with double bonds are called **alkenes**. They are **unsaturated** because they have a double bond.
(Remember **saturated** compounds have all single bonds.)

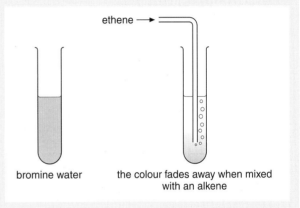

heptane → crack → pentane + ethene

notice the double bond in the middle of the ethene molecule

Testing for a double bond

Alkenes are unsaturated because other molecules can be added on. This is called an **addition** reaction. Ethene is an alkene.

ethene + bromine → dibromoethane

$$C=C + Br_2 \longrightarrow H-C-C-H$$

Dibromoethane is colourless; the orange colour disappears.

ethene →

bromine water

the colour fades away when mixed with an alkene

?

Things to do

2   Heptane can also be cracked to make propene, C_3H_6. Propene is an **unsaturated** alkene with a double bond. Use structural formulas to write an equation to show how heptane can be cracked to make propene. What is the name of the other molecule made at the same time? Is the other molecule an alkane or an alkene?

3   This letter appeared in a local paper.

Suppose you were working in the customer relations department at the oil refinery. Write a letter to the paper to explain the refinery's point of view. Try to answer all the criticisms of the 'furious local resident'.

Letter to the editor

I am speechless at the news that the local oil refinery is building a large new section for cracking. Another eyesore! More of our countryside spoiled! Why does the oil industry care so little about polluting our environment? I understand the thing will be running day and night at 800 °C.

What a waste of fuel! Don't they realise our fossil fuels are running out and should be saved? I suppose they'll increase petrol prices to pay for it.

Furious local resident

Addition polymers (SS) MU11

Polymers are long-chain molecules, made when lots of small molecules (**monomers**) join together. Alkenes can make polymers because they have double bonds between carbon atoms. The double bonds open up and join the molecules together. This is called an **addition** reaction.

part of a polyethene molecule

All these containers are made of polyethene.

Separate monomer molecules join to form a polyethene chain. The chains can be very long, sometimes more than 50 000 carbon atoms long!

You can also write formulas using brackets to show how long chains of polyethene are formed from separate ethene molecules.

? Things to do

1   Bobby tested ethene and polyethene with bromine water. The bromine water turned colourless in ethene, but stayed orange with polyethene. Explain why.

2   Explain why ethene is a gas, but polyethene is a solid.

3   Other addition polymers can also be made from monomers containing carbon–carbon double bonds. Look at the structures of these two monomers.

vinyl chloride   propene

   a   What are the names of the polymers made from these monomers?

   b   Draw the structures of the polymers using both ways of showing the polymer.

   c   Find out what these polymers are used for.

The discovery of polyethene

Reg Gibson and Eric Fawcett were two chemists working for ICI in the 1930s. They were trying to develop new dyes by reacting carbon compounds together in high pressure apparatus. They sometimes used pressures of about 2000 times atmospheric pressure! One Friday night in 1932 they put some ethene in the high pressure reactor with another compound called benzaldehyde. By accident, they had also got some air into the apparatus. They left the reaction to run over the weekend, hoping to make a new dye. When they returned on Monday morning, they were irritated to find their experiment had 'gone wrong'. All that was left in the reactor was a small amount of a white, waxy solid. We now know this was polyethene.

The two chemists recorded their results, but could not get the reaction to work again reliably (it kept exploding!). They lost interest and went back to making new dyes. Three years later, another chemist working with them realised that the waxy solid might be a very useful material. He persuaded them to try again. He thought the air leak was important (he was right – oxygen is needed to make the reaction work). After a great deal of adapting and research, ICI were ready to mass produce polyethene. We now use tonnes every day. From washing up bowls to radar equipment to carrier bags – our lives would be very different without it!

Eric Fawcett (shown here) and Reg Gibson were experimenting with the production of dyes when they accidentally made polyethene in 1932.

? Things to do

4 Polyethene now has many uses where it has replaced earlier materials like wood, glass, paper or metals.

   a Look round your home and make a list of things made of polyethene.

   b For each one you find, decide what material it might have been made of before polyethene was invented.

   c Describe the advantages of polyethene in each case, compared with the older material it has replaced.

5 Look at these notes about the experiments which 'went wrong' when Gibson and Fawcett first tried to make polyethene:

   - *very high pressure is needed to make anything happen*
   - *the mixture contained ethane, benzaldehyde and air*
   - *the reaction makes a lot of heat and the temperature rises*
   - *if it gets too hot it may explode*

   Make plans for experiments to discover:

   a which substances are needed to make the reaction work

   b how the reaction can be controlled to avoid explosions.

   Say what materials you would use in each experiment.

8 A different type of polymer

Condensation polymers (SS) MU12

Small molecules which have double bonds can simply be put together to make polymers. Even when there is no suitable double bond available, molecules can sometimes be made to link together, but some atoms have to be moved out of the way first, so that bonds are left free to form the new link.

For example, nylon is made from two rather complicated chemicals:

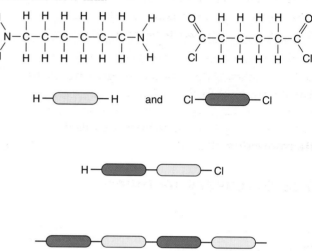

It is only the atoms on the ends of the molecules which are involved in polymerisation, so the structure can be shown more simply as:

When these react, a hydrogen atom from one molecule joins with a chlorine atom from the other to form hydrogen chloride. The two monomers can then join together as the first step in forming a polymer chain:

This short chain still has a reactive atom at each end, so it can go on growing!

This type of polymerisation, where atoms have to be removed to let the polymer chain grow, is called **condensation polymerisation.**

You may also have noticed another difference between polyethene and nylon. To make polyethene, all of the monomer molecules were the same (ethene), but in making this type of nylon, two different monomers have been used. It is called a **co-polymer.** By carefully choosing different monomers, chemists can make polymers that have many different properties.

This illustration is from a poster used in 1949 to advertise nylon. All the garments are made of nylon, including the stockings.

Thermosoftening and thermosetting polymers

Polyethene and nylon are both long thin molecules. These can move past each other and slide fairly easily, so the plastics are not hard, and are easily softened and melted by heating them. When heated, they can easily be rolled into thin sheets (for example, for making plastic bags) or stretched into threads (such as nylon thread, or polypropene fibre for making carpets). Plastics of this type are called **thermosoftening** polymers.

The freely moving molecules in a thermosoftening polymer.

Some polymers are made from monomers which can form **cross-links** between the growing chains. These cross-links fix the molecules together to form a hard, rigid structure. The cross-links are often formed by heating, so these are called **thermosetting** plastics.

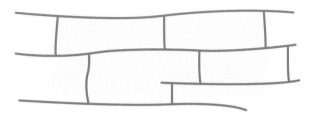
The more rigid molecules in a thermosetting polymer.

The discovery of nylon

In 1935, a chemist called Wallace Carothers discovered **nylon** when he was deliberately trying to find a substitute for silk (which is very expensive).

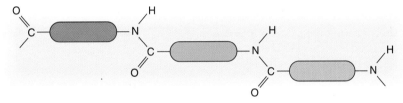
Part of a protein chain showing three amino acids linked together.

Silk is a **protein**. It has lots of different **amino acids** joined together (the particular arrangement of four atoms which join the amino acids in proteins is called a peptide link).

Caruthers experimented by reacting together different monomers. Eventually, he found a co-polymer made from two different monomers (shown on page 58) formed a polymer chain that could be melted and stretched into fine threads.

The structure of nylon is much simpler than that of silk, but the new material soon found many uses. Unlike silk, nylon can be melted and cast into complex shapes. For example, gear wheels made of nylon work very smoothly and are often used in food mixing machinery because they do not need oiling, so there is no risk of contaminating the food.

Silk is a natural fibre made from the threads spun by silk worms.

In WW2, so much nylon was used for making parachutes that there was none left for nylon stockings – some women stained their legs with gravy powder to make it look as if they were wearing stockings!

Making plastic bottles

The plastic used to make fizzy drinks bottles is called polyethylene terephthalate (PETE for short). It is a **thermoplastic** and so can be shaped by heating it up to melt it.

Look at the flow chart to see how a PETE bottle is manufactured. The process involves injection and blow moulding.

If you look on the bottom of a fizzy drinks bottle you will see a raised circle where the hot melted plastic was injected into the mould.

You may also see a recycling symbol like the one shown here.

This tells you that the bottle is made from PETE.

Look at the flowscheme. At what stages would you need to heat the PETE?

Make a list of reasons why PETE is a good material to use for drink bottles.

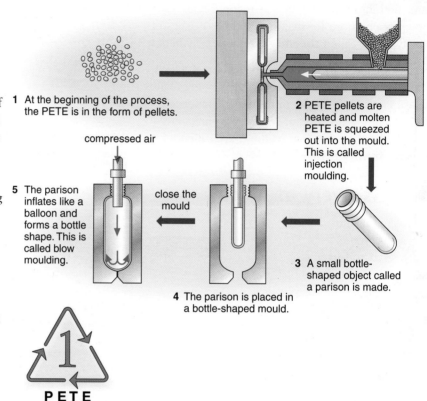

1 At the beginning of the process, the PETE is in the form of pellets.

2 PETE pellets are heated and molten PETE is squeezed out into the mould. This is called injection moulding.

compressed air

5 The parison inflates like a balloon and forms a bottle shape. This is called blow moulding.

close the mould

3 A small bottle-shaped object called a parison is made.

4 The parison is placed in a bottle-shaped mould.

PETE

? Things to do

Plastic packaging very quickly ends up in the bin. In this country most of our household waste is buried in **landfill sites** or **incinerated**. Discuss these questions with your group. You might also ask these questions at home with your family and see if different generations have different opinions about recycling materials.

1   Do you think plastic bottles should be recycled?

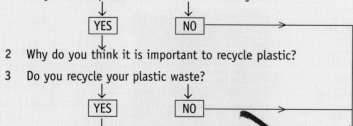

YES   NO

2   Why do you think it is important to recycle plastic?

3   Do you recycle your plastic waste?

YES   NO

4   If you do recycle, do you find it easy to do? Explain why.

5   What stops you from recycling your plastic?

Is it worth recycling PETE drinks bottles? (SS) MU13

A city council wants to set up a recycling scheme for plastic bottles. A local recycling company is willing to work with the council to make PETE pellets. The pellets can be sold to a local packaging factory. At the moment the packaging factory can buy 'new' pellets for £675 per 800 kg.

The table shows what costs the council and the recycling company would have in making the pellets.

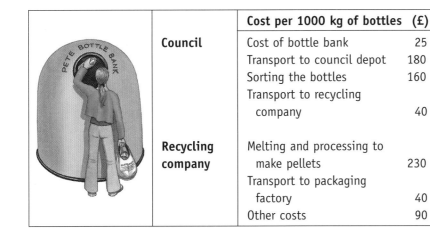

		Cost per 1000 kg of bottles (£)	
	Council	Cost of bottle bank	25
		Transport to council depot	180
		Sorting the bottles	160
		Transport to recycling company	40
	Recycling company	Melting and processing to make pellets	230
		Transport to packaging factory	40
		Other costs	90

1000 kg of bottles make 800 kg of 'recycled' pellets

Are there any other benefits? (SS) MU14

The costs given above are only the direct costs of the recycling. What other factors should be considered?

- If the bottles are not recycled, there will be more rubbish to collect and dispose of, and this will put up the cost of rubbish disposal – should you take account of this too?
- If bottles are recycled, less new plastic is needed and so less oil needs to be used.

?

Things to do

6   Write a flow chart to show what happens to a bottle after it is put in a bottle bank. Finish your flow chart with the plastic being made again into a new bottle.

7   The recycling scheme shown above is 'running at a loss'. Work out the total cost of making 800 kg of recycled pellets. How much money is lost?

8   Look at your flow chart. Can the scheme be adapted to save costs?

9   Write a leaflet which the council could use to persuade people that recycling plastic bottles is a good thing.

1 The table shows information about some compounds.

Name	Number of carbon atoms in molecules	Boiling point (°C)
methane	1	–161
ethane	2	–88
propane	3	–42
butane	4	0
pentane	5	36
hexane	6	69
heptane	7	99

a Which of these words fit the compounds in the table?

**saturated   unsaturated   alkanes
alkenes   fuels   hydrocarbons**

b Write down the formulas for propane and octane.

c Plot a graph of number of carbon atoms against boiling point for these compounds.

d The temperature in the UK varies between about 30 °C and –10 °C. Mark these temperatures on your graph. What is the physical state of each compound at 30 °C and at –10 °C?

e Bottled gas for camping stoves contains butane. Why is it more difficult to light a camping stove on a cold frosty morning?

2 John boiled some water and took the temperature every minute. This is a graph of his results.

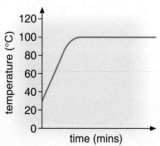

a What happens to the temperature of water while it is boiling?

b Use the table in Question 1 to help you. Draw a graph to show how the temperature would change when a mixture of hexane, heptane and octane is heated.

c How could you separate the three fuels?

3 Use the formulas below to answer the questions.

chloromethane   H—C—Cl

propene

O=C—O—H   aspirin

ethanol ('alcohol' in drinks)

a Which molecules are saturated?

b Which would decolorize bromine water?

c Which molecule is a hydrocarbon?

d The simplest formula for ethanol is C_2H_6O. What is the simplest formula for aspirin?

e Propene can be made into a polymer which is used to make carpets and measuring cylinders.

   i What is the name of the polymer?

   ii Draw the structure of the polymer.

4 The table shows the contents of household rubbish as percentage by weight.

Material	% by weight of rubbish
paper and board	35%
food and garden waste	25%
plastic	6%
glass	8%
metal	6%
other	20%

a Use the data to draw a bar chart.

b If the percentages had been worked out by volume of the waste, how would this have changed the percentage of plastic waste?

c What percentage of the rubbish will have rotted away after 50 years?

INTRODUCING

Waste not, want not

Try these first

1 Enzymes are vital to living organisms because:

  a they are all proteins

  b they speed up body reactions

  c they work according to the lock and key theory.

2 Respiration is:

  a the way plants make their food

  b the way we breathe

  c the chemical oxidation of food to release energy.

3 The main nutrient elements in fertilisers are:

  a N, K & P   b N, S & Na   c K, Fe & P

4 Microbes grow best in the following conditions:

  a cool, dry and light

  b warm, moist and light

  c warm, moist and plenty of food.

Domestic waste has attracted foxes into towns.

Waste is emptied into landfill sites which are then landscaped to blend into the surroundings.

In this unit you will learn:

- about the importance of microbes in decomposition
- why waste disposal is a problem
- how waste water is treated
- about reclaiming useful materials from rubbish
- about the carbon and nitrogen cycles
- how human actions affect the recycling of nitrogen and carbon.

1 How does nature deal with waste?

What happens to waste? WW1

Modern lifestyles make a lot of waste: left-over bits of food, old clothes, empty bottles and bags and so on. Getting rid of waste can be a problem. You may have seen rubbish just dumped in the countryside or on the streets. What will happen to it? How much will be still there in a day? A week? A year?

Some waste materials are broken down naturally by microbes. They are said to be **biodegradable**. Others cannot be broken down naturally. They are **non-biodegradable**.

Natural waste – dead plants and animal remains

Think about all the trees in your area. Each year, many of them grow leaves which die and fall off in autumn. They do this every year. What happens to all the leaves which pile up every autumn? The answer is that they rot away, or **decompose**. The leaves have disappeared, they have been broken down into simple compounds like the ones they were originally made from. All living things eventually die and decompose. Decomposition is a natural process which recycles chemicals that are essential to life, so that they can be used as nutrients by future generations of plants. If it were not for decomposition, we should be surrounded by dead things!

Hooray for decomposers!

Decomposition is a biological process and it depends on living organisms which feed on dead organic materials. They are called **saprophytes**, and some of the most important ones are **bacteria** or **fungi**.

Plants need chemicals called nutrients for growth. These are found in the soil. You studied some of them in the unit called *Food for thought* (Y10). The nutrients are passed on to animals when they eat the plants, forming food chains and webs, which you studied in the unit *Balancing acts* (Y10). Eventually, the soil would run out of nutrients, but the decomposers provide the vital link to recycle nutrients back into the soil again.

It only takes a small amount of waste for a roadside area to become a dumping ground.

This tree stump has started to decompose and provides a source of nutrients for the fungi growing on it.

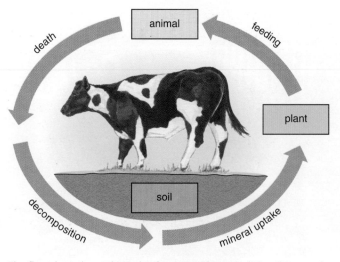

The flow chart shows the cycle of nutrients between living things and dead materials.

Decomposers work by producing enzymes that can break down fats, carbohydrate, protein and other organic substances. These enzymes work in the same way as those in your gut, but decomposers are tiny and do not have their own guts. Instead, they release their enzymes onto the rotting material, so it is digested outside their bodies. They absorb some of the nutrients that are formed as food for themselves, but some is left and spreads out into the soil.

What conditions speed up decomposition? (SS) WW2

Decomposition reactions are catalysed by the enzymes given out by decomposers. How much do you remember about enzymes? Enzyme action depends on a very exact fit between the **active site** on the enzyme molecule and its **substrate** (the substance it reacts with). Because of this, enzymes are very **specific**: they will catalyse one reaction only. Decomposition processes involve many stages, and each will need a separate enzyme.

Enzymes are proteins, with large, complex molecules. The shape of the molecule is easily altered by changes in acidity or temperature. If enzymes are heated much above their normal working temperature, the shape of the molecule can be permanently changed, so that the enzyme will not work. It is said to be **denatured**.

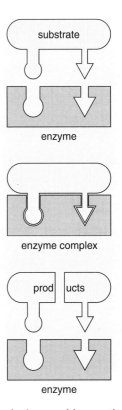

Stages in decomposition reaction. Each reaction is catalysed by a specific enzyme.

F

Decomposition reactions are favoured by warmth and damp. Organic wastes break down faster in these conditions.

?

Things to do

1   Name three nutrient elements which plants take up from the soil.

2   Re-draw the diagram opposite that shows how nutrients are recycled. Add labels to identify producers, consumers and decomposers in the cycle (it may help to look at *Balancing acts*, Y10).

3   Compost is a useful fertiliser made from decomposed plant material. Gardeners make compost using containers with holes in. They put in layers of vegetable waste, separated by layers of soil. The containers are often left with the tops open.

   a   What is provided in the layers of soil?

   b   Why are the containers left open?

   c   Decomposition reactions in compost liberate heat and make the compost heap warm. How does this help the process?

2 Life depends on carbon

The chemistry of life

Carbon is a very special element because carbon atoms are able to link to one another to form chains of different lengths, and they can also bond to atoms of other elements such as hydrogen, oxygen, nitrogen or sulphur. This makes it possible to build up molecules such as carbohydrates, fats, proteins and many other complicated substances necessary for life. Because these substances are found in living organisms, they are called **organic** chemicals and they all depend on carbon.

Photosynthesis and respiration – the ebb and flow of life

The most important process for creating organic compounds from simple starting materials is **photosynthesis**. Through many stages of reaction, carbon dioxide and water are gradually combined to form glucose, a sugar, and oxygen.

The unit *Staying alive* (Y11) gives more details of photosynthesis, but the whole process can be summed up by the equation:

$$6CO_2 + 6H_2O \rightarrow C_6H_{12}O_6 + 6O_2$$

Most of the stages in photosynthesis are **endothermic** and need a supply of energy to make them work. This energy comes from sunlight.

Plants and animals get the energy they need for other life processes by reversing this process. Glucose is broken down to carbon dioxide and water again. The process is called **respiration** and can be summarised by the equation:

$$C_6H_{12}O_6 + 6O_2 \rightarrow 6CO_2 + 6H_2O$$

Notice that this is the reverse of photosynthesis. When a chemical reaction is reversed, the accompanying energy change is also reversed. Energy from sunlight is taken in by photosynthesis, and an equivalent amount of energy is given out by respiration.

Carbon forms part of the complex DNA molecule which has a structure like a double helix.

Trees in tropical rainforests take in huge amounts of carbon dioxide from the atmosphere.

? Things to do

1 **a** Make a list of the limiting factors which affect the rate of photosynthesis

   b With your group, discuss how the rate of growth of trees and forests might be affected if the concentration of carbon dioxide in the atmosphere changed.

Carbon on the move WW3

Notice that carbon dioxide is the starter material for making organic compounds, and it is also the waste product when they break down. Because carbon dioxide is a gas, it can spread through the atmosphere and form part of a great cycle of carbon compounds called the **carbon cycle**. This is nature's way of recycling carbon from dead plants and animals so that it is made available again for more photosynthesis.

Respiration in your body cells goes on all the time. The carbon dioxide, which is a waste product, is removed by breathing it out. If your breath is passed through limewater, the limewater goes cloudy.

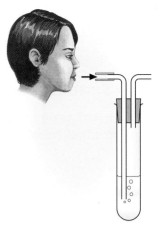

The carbon dioxide in air breathed out turns limewater cloudy.

Carbon locked up

The equation for respiration shows that oxygen is needed to convert all the carbon in organic compounds back into carbon dioxide. When animal or plant remains are covered and kept away from the air, some bacteria (anaerobic bacteria) can still make use of them as food. However, anaerobic respiration can only partly break down the compounds. Less carbon dioxide (sometimes none) is formed and the carbon compounds remain locked up and are not returned to the atmosphere. This is how fossil fuels, such as coal or oil, are formed. When coal or oil are burned, this carbon is returned back into the atmosphere.

As fuel is burned carbon dioxide is released into the atmosphere and the carbon becomes 'available'.

? Things to do

2   A gardener grows flowers from seed. At the end of the summer, she tidies the garden by burning the dead plants. Explain whether this will make a difference to the amount of carbon dioxide in the air.

3   How would the amount of carbon dioxide in the air be affected if:

    a   Large areas of rain-forest are cut down

    b   The area of desert in the World increases?

4   Lime (calcium oxide) is made by heating limestone (calcium carbonate).

    a   Write a balanced chemical equation for this reaction.

    b   The carbon dioxide which is formed escapes into the air. Two million tonnes of lime are made every year in the UK. Calculate how much carbon dioxide this adds to the atmosphere.

Sinks, sources and reservoirs (SS) WW4

One way to monitor carbon as it moves round the carbon cycle is to track what happens to carbon dioxide.

The level of carbon dioxide in the air has a great effect on the rate of photosynthesis and on global temperatures (remember the unit *Restless Earth*). Various different **reservoirs** can hold large amounts of carbon compounds.

The sea

Carbon dioxide is soluble in water. It is only slightly soluble, but there is a lot of sea! Seven-tenths of the Earth's surface is covered with water and this large surface allows carbon dioxide to dissolve, and also to evaporate again.

The seas act as a **reservoir** to hold large amounts of dissolved carbon dioxide, and also as a **sink** to absorb the gas from the air, or a **source** to release some of it back into the air.

Plants in the sea make use of dissolved carbon dioxide for photosynthesis. Many sea animals absorb carbon dioxide from water and use it in making shells, which consist mainly of calcium carbonate.

Remains of sea creatures or plants become buried in the sediment at the bottom of the sea. The soft organic parts are decomposed by anaerobic bacteria, forming oil and methane. The shells are crushed and cemented together, forming rocks such as chalk or limestone.

Oil and gas form a reservoir of carbon which can be released if we extract and burn them. Carbonate rocks lock up carbon for a very long time.

The oceans play a very important part in balancing the carbon cycle and any change in sea water temperature could have a big effect on world climates.

Plant life

The growth of plants removes large amounts of carbon dioxide from the air. Decay of plant or animal remains returns this carbon dioxide back to the air. Forests hold a great deal of carbon as compounds, like cellulose in wood. Humans can have an effect on the amount of carbon stored in this reservoir by the way we manage forests and agriculture.

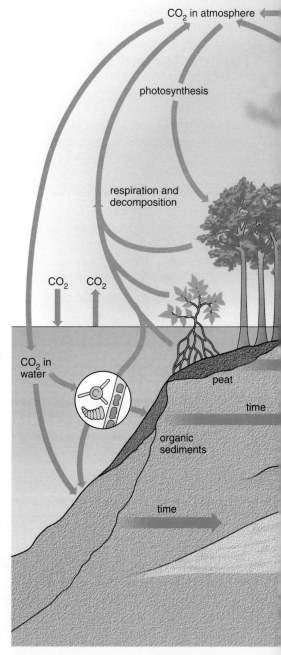

There is a natural system for recycling carbon. Green plants absorb carbon during photosynthesis, animals and plants release it during respiration and when they decay.

Coal

Coal has been formed from the remains of forests that grew in warm, swampy areas. Wood that became buried under mud and sediment gradually turned into coal, which is mostly carbon. As long as the coal remains buried, this carbon is removed from the carbon cycle. When coal is burned, we are adding to the carbon dioxide in the atmosphere.

Recovering carbon from rocks

In the unit *Restless Earth* (Y10), you learned that movements of tectonic plates can push seafloor sediments up to form mountains. Mount Everest is formed from rock which was once below the sea floor!

When carbonate rocks are exposed to the air, they can be gradually dissolved away. The carbon in the dissolved rock is returned to the sea, in a form which can be used by sea plants and animals. Even the carbon which is locked up in rocks can be recycled, but this is a very slow part of the system.

? Things to do

1   Make a list of all the processes that remove carbon dioxide from the atmosphere.

2   Make a list of all the processes that release carbon dioxide into the air.

3   For both of these lists, discuss which processes are likely to be affected most by human activity.

4   Millions of tonnes of limestone (calcium carbonate) are used every year. Some is heated to form lime, some is used as limestone for building. How will each of these processes affect the amount of carbon dioxide in the air?

5   Write a diary of the adventures of a carbon atom, starting when it is part of a carbon dioxide molecule breathed out by a vocalist at a pop concert, and ending when it is part of a slice of bread made from wheat grown in a distant country.

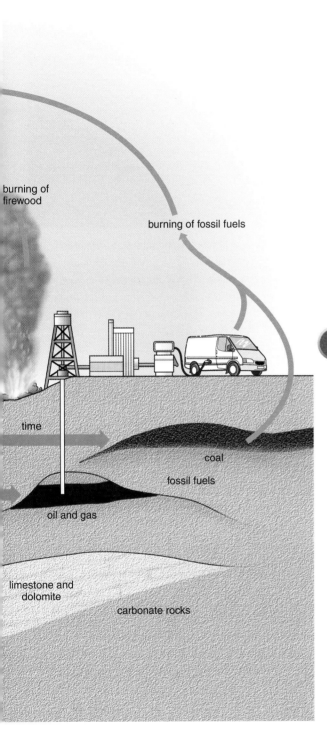

burning of firewood

burning of fossil fuels

time

coal

fossil fuels

oil and gas

limestone and dolomite

carbonate rocks

4 Disturbing the carbon cycle

Human activity and the carbon cycle

Everything we do has some effect on the environment, but there are two very important ways in which our actions affect the carbon cycle:

- destruction of forests
- increased burning of fossil fuels.

Most of the world's tropical rainforest is in the Amazon Basin. It covers an area about two-thirds the size of the USA. Because the forests are so large, and grow so quickly, they play an important part in keeping down the amount of carbon dioxide in the atmosphere. The forests seem very large, but there is only half as much rainforest as there used to be and it is being reduced at a rate of about 20 million hectares per year.

Some of the wood is hardwood, which is used for timber, but the main reason for felling the trees and clearing the land is to use it for agriculture and building.

Destruction of rainforests means that there is an increase in the amount of carbon dioxide in the atmosphere. The effect is an increase in atmospheric temperature as carbon dioxide absorbs heat energy.

Carbon in fossil fuels has been 'locked up' for millions of years. Increasing industrial activity and higher living standards have led to rapid increases in the amount of fossil fuel extracted and burned. In turn, this leads to more carbon dioxide in the air. World governments are seeking agreement to control or reduce carbon dioxide emissions, but solutions are not easy to find.

Why does it matter? – The greenhouse effect

Since carbon dioxide in the air is essential for photosynthesis, why should we bother if the amount increases? In the unit *Restless Earth* (Y10), you saw this graph. It shows that the radiation received by Earth from the Sun (a very hot body) has shorter wavelengths than the radiation given out by the Earth (which is much cooler).

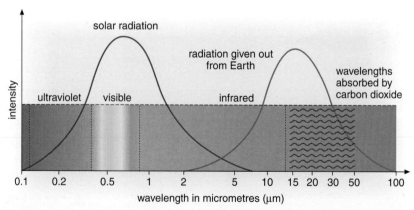

The Earth absorbs radiation of short wavelength from the Sun and gives out radiation of longer wavelength.

It is the balance between radiation into and out of the atmosphere which determines the surface temperature of the Earth. Gases in the atmosphere absorb and trap some of the longer wavelength radiation, in just the same way that the glass of a greenhouse reduces the amount of heat that escapes. This **greenhouse effect** is essential to life. Without it, our planet would be so cold that all the water would be frozen.

However, notice that carbon dioxide absorbs infrared radiation. The more carbon dioxide in the atmosphere, the more energy will be trapped. The effects of this are difficult to predict, which is the reason why scientists and governments are worried about increases in carbon dioxide levels.

Would global warming be a problem?

These headlines have appeared in newspapers in recent years:

Fears of rise in sea levels rejected

No one knows for sure how soon, or how much, world temperatures may change due to air pollution, but some say there may be benefits, with increased temperatures and increased carbon dioxide levels leading to larger crop yields.

What worries scientists is that the amount of carbon dioxide in the atmosphere is changing, and this will almost certainly cause changes in world weather patterns.

The surface of the Earth has warmed by 0.7 °C over the last century and there are fears that this warming is increasing.

If the temperature of the Arctic and Antarctic were to rise above 0 °C, then the polar ice would melt. At the Antarctic the ice is on top of land. Therefore, if it did melt, it would cause a rise in sea level. Many low-lying areas, including London, would be flooded.

It's tough keeping cool!

Things to do

This graph shows carbon dioxide concentrations in air at one place in Europe from 1956–91.

1 How much has the concentration of carbon dioxide changed between 1960 and 1990?

2 Why do you think carbon dioxide levels are higher in winter than in summer?

3 Discuss how each of these actions might affect the level of carbon dioxide in the atmosphere.

   a Walking to the shops instead of going by car.

   b Turning down the thermostat on oil-fired central heating.

   c Turning down the thermostat on electric heating.

   d Planting some trees.

   e Using the same carrier bag many times when shopping.

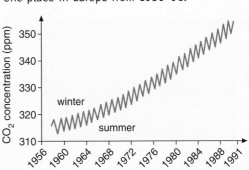

5 Nitrogen goes round and round too!

The nitrogen cycle WW5, WW6, WW7

All living things contain proteins. All proteins contain nitrogen. Life therefore could not exist without nitrogen, and nitrogen becomes another of the important chemicals recycled by nature.

About 80% of the Earth's atmosphere is nitrogen, but it is very unreactive. The atoms are tightly linked in pairs (N_2) and not easy to separate. Most living things cannot use nitrogen gas directly. Once again, bacteria come to the rescue. There are bacteria living in the soil, which are described as **nitrogen-fixing bacteria**. They use atmospheric nitrogen to make nitrates, which can be taken up by plant roots and used to make plant proteins. Animals get their nitrogen in the form of proteins in the food they eat. Some nitrogen is fixed by the energy contained in lightning. It combines with oxygen and comes to the soil dissolved in rainwater.

Animal and plant remains contain protein. This protein is broken down by decomposers to release ammonia. **Nitrite bacteria** in the soil convert ammonium compounds into nitrites by combining them with oxygen. **Nitrate bacteria** in the soil convert nitrites to nitrates by adding more oxygen. The nitrite and nitrate bacteria are jointly called **nitrifying bacteria**, and the nitrates they produce can be used by plants.

There are also some bacteria living in the soil which convert nitrates back into nitrogen gas which is lost back into the atmosphere. These are called **denitrifying bacteria**.

proteins in dead animals

denitrifying bacteria in the soil convert nitrates back into nitrogen

saprophytes turn proteins into ammonia. **nitrifying** bacteria turn ammonia into nitrites and then nitrates in the soil

animals die, and produce faeces

proteins in animals

animals eat plants

? Things to do

1   'Organic' farmers do not use manufactured chemical fertilisers. Suggest and explain ways they could use to increase the nitrate content of their soil.

2   Denitrifying bacteria are anaerobic. Suggest why heavy, waterlogged soils tend to be less productive than better-drained, well-aerated soils.

3   Look back to your notes on the unit *Food for thought* (Y10). Write a chemical equation for the main reaction in the Haber process, and explain why the process is important for agriculture.

ammonia factory

lightning

root nodules

lightning converts nitrogen in the air to oxides of nitrogen. These are washed into the soil and form nitrates

nitrogen gets from the atmosphere to the soil by **nitrogen-fixing bacteria,** fertilisers and **lightning**

leguminous crops such as peas and beans have root nodules. Leguminous crops can grow in nitrogen-poor soil

root nodules contain *Rhizobium* bacteria which are **nitrogen-fixing bacteria**. They convert nitrogen from the air to nitrates in the soil

fertilisers in soil

plant roots absorb nitrates from the soil. Plants make proteins

plants die

farmers use **fertilisers** and manure to put nitrogen into the soil

some leached into waterways

proteins in plants

Root nodules on peas, beans or clover (**leguminous** plants) contain *Rhizobium* bacteria which are nitrogen-fixing bacteria. They can turn nitrogen from the air into nitrates in the soil.

The relationship between root nodule bacteria and leguminous plants is of benefit to both – it is symbiotic. The bacteria get shelter and food from the plants, the plants get a supply of nitrates.

Human activity affects the nitrogen cycle. If farmers remove crops, the nitrogen they contain is not returned to the soil. This is why nitrogen-containing fertilisers are added to the soil, to keep it fertile. Either manufactured chemicals or manure or compost may be used.

Another way to keep up soil fertility is **crop rotation**. One year, legumes are grown, to put nitrates into the soil. For one or two years afterwards other crops can be grown, before the rotation is begun again.

Nitrogen goes round and round too!

6 What's in your bin?

The things you throw away

Every year, families in Britain throw away 20 million tonnes of domestic waste. What sort of things do you throw away?

Look at the details of what an average family throws out in a week.

Do you really have to throw so much away? There are four main ways of disposing of unwanted items.

	% by mass	kg per week
glass	10	1.6
paper	25	4.0
metal	15	2.4
plastic	4	0.6
textiles	4	0.6
food waste	31	5.0
dust/cinders	5	0.8
others	6	1.0

Contents and relative proportions in household waste.

Can it be reused?

Some things could be sorted, cleaned and used again (e.g. old toys could be passed to another child – or even sold!). This requires time and effort to sort and store the items, and to make contact with potential new owners. But, it means less rubbish to be removed, less damage to the environment and it may even make some money for you!

Recycling

Materials can be recovered for use again (for example waste paper can be pulped and made into 'recycled paper'). Sorting and separating materials requires time and effort, but recycling saves on raw materials and often requires much less energy than making new material from raw materials.

Examples of materials that can be recycled.

Incineration (burning)

The rubbish is burned. The volume of material then left to dispose of is much smaller. Specially designed furnaces are needed. Sometimes the energy released can be used for heating. Care is needed to keep down dust, or harmful chemicals.

Landfill

The waste is tipped into special sites such as old quarries, then buried with soil. Care is needed to avoid polluting local waterways.

Rubbish may be burned but material still has to be buried.

> **?**
>
> ## Things to do
>
> 1 Make a list of things thrown out from your home during a week (such as, stale bread, vacuum-cleaner dust, plastic bags, potato peel, empty bottles, drinks cans, and so on). Discuss which of the four disposal methods would be best for each of the items on your list.
>
> 2 Make a list of recycling facilities you know about in your area, where they are and what can be recycled at each one.

Old quarries are often used as landfill sites.

Waste not, want not

Keeping Britain tidy

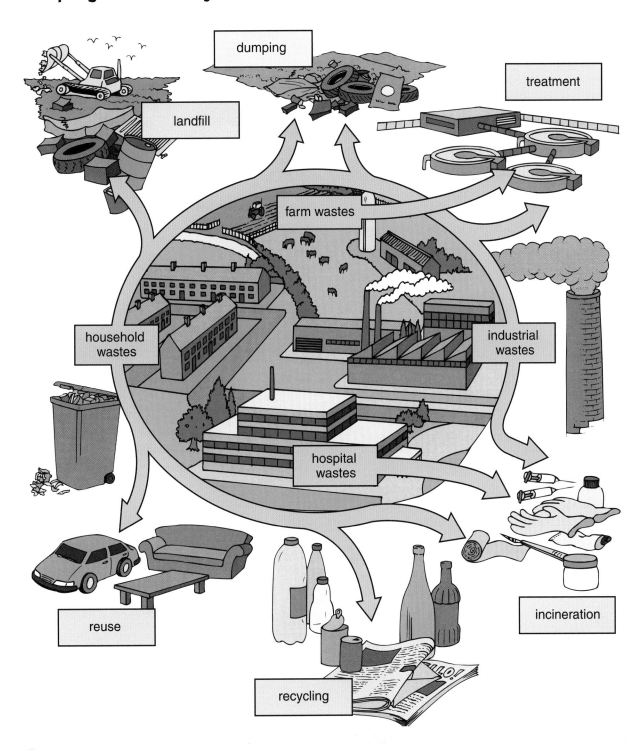

dumping

treatment

landfill

farm wastes

household wastes

industrial wastes

hospital wastes

incineration

reuse

recycling

?

Things to do

3   Which of these processes goes on in your neighbourhood? Discuss the advantages and disadvantages of each way of disposing of waste.

Landfill waste disposal

Most of our rubbish is taken to a 'tip' or landfill site. This may be an old quarry or pit, which is being filled in with rubbish. Some sites are specially dug and lined so that any contaminated water from the site can be safely piped away for treatment.

A typical landfill site will be covered in plastic carrier bags!

As each area of the site is filled the rubbish is compressed and covered with rubble and soil. Microbes (mainly bacteria) feed on the rubbish in the tip and decompose the biodegradable parts. Some of these bacteria respire without oxygen, they are **anaerobic**. They gain their energy by reducing carbohydrates or carbon dioxide to methane, but only in the absence of oxygen. There is no oxygen at the bottom of a rubbish tip therefore these bacteria thrive.

The methane they produce moves upwards through the tip. Methane is a flammable gas and can form an explosive mixture with air. Frequently, landfill sites have large blue flames where the methane is vented and burned off. In some cases, if sufficient methane is released, it is actually put to a use, for example, to generate electricity.

Methane from an old landfill site provides energy for this electricity generator.

One problem with landfill, is what to do with the site once it has been filled and capped. In most areas it is returned to agricultural use because it remains too unstable for building purposes. A second problem is that we are rapidly running out of suitable sites for landfill.

Even where building may be possible on old landfill sites, care must be taken to avoid build up of methane escaping into the buildings.

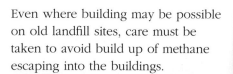

? Things to do

1   Look up the formula of methane and write an equation for the reaction when methane burns completely.

2   Why might problems arise if a landfill site was close to a stream or river?

The house which was built here, on an old landfill site, was destroyed when methane gas seeped up into it and exploded.

Keeping down the volume of waste

Dealing with waste costs money, and the more waste there is, the more money it costs! How can you make choices which will help to keep costs down and save valuable materials?

One choice is the type of bag you use to carry your shopping. Plastic carrier bags are usually made of polyethene.

Polyethene is made from ethene, which in turn is made from oil. Oil takes millions of years to form from the remains of tiny dead sea creatures. It is a **non-renewable** resource and we are using it up very quickly.

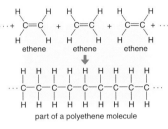

An alternative is to use paper bags. These can be made from recycled paper. Paper is made from wood, which is shredded and pulped with water, then rolled into flat sheets. Fast-growing trees provide continuous supplies of wood. Woody parts of plants contain a lot of cellulose, a polymer made by linking glucose molecules together. Paper is mainly cellulose.

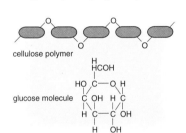

You also have a third alternative: you can buy a much stronger bag and carry it with you every time you go shopping!

? Things to do

3   Look at the shop scene. What do you think people mean by 'environmentally friendly'?

4   Discuss which comments you agree with. What sort of bag do you think is best?

5   There is not always a clear distinction between what is a renewable resource and what is a non-renewable resource. Using the examples of wood and oil, explain what is meant by this statement.

6   You are a supermarket manager. Write a leaflet to be distributed to customers explaining why you are now using paper bags instead of plastic ones. Outline any other measures your supermarket might take to conserve natural resources.

7   There are glass bottle banks in most towns, but you do not see many plastic banks. Why do you think recycling plastic is less common than recycling glass?

8   Discuss the advantages and disadvantages of collecting rubbish in plastic sacks rather than emptying metal bins.

What happens to waste water? (SS) WW8, WW9, WW10

In addition to all the rubbish we produce, each household produces a large quantity of waste water every day.

Domestic waste water (sewage) contains human waste (faeces, urine and so on), soaps, detergents, vegetable and food waste, soil, paper, dissolved salts and assorted other materials.

As urine and faeces carry bacteria, which may cause disease, careful treatment of waste water is necessary to avoid the spread of disease.

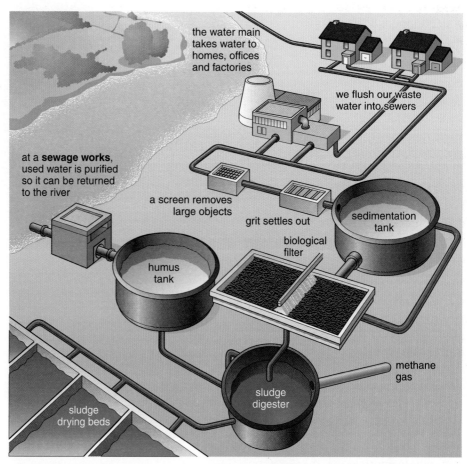

Water is recycled. As a river flows to the sea, water may be removed, used, purified and returned to it as many as six or seven times.

Stages in sewage treatment

Screening: where solid debris is removed. This is a sort of filtering which separates out larger pieces of debris such as sticks, cans, rags etc. Smaller pieces of grit are allowed to settle out before being washed and used as a building material.

Primary treatment: where the waste water is allowed to stand in sedimentation tanks for 10–12 hours. Suspended solids gradually settle and the whole process is speeded up by the addition of aluminium sulphate which helps the solids stick together (coagulate).

Biological filtration (not really a filtering process at all!): where the waste water trickles down through about two metres of stones. The stones are covered with bacteria, which digest the organic material in the water. The bacteria are aerobic which means they need oxygen. The stones provide a large surface area for the waste water to trickle over. In this way it comes into contact with the bacteria and oxygen.

Settling: where the liquid is then left to settle in tanks called humus tanks. The water coming from these tanks is checked and if it is sufficiently pure it is allowed to run into a river. If not, it is treated again.

Sludge digestion: here bacteria digest what remains from the other stages. These bacteria are anaerobic so the digestion tanks are kept airtight. The process produces methane gas, which can be used as a fuel. The sludge that results is dried and can be used as a fertiliser.

Waste not, want not

In a modern, industrial society, waste is big business. Unnecessary use of materials not only uses up precious resources, it leads to pollution problems and enormous costs in clearing away waste. We have a long way to go before we can match the efficiency with which nature recycles materials.

In planning to achieve **sustainable development**, which avoids long-term harm to the environment, it is necessary to think of the whole life-cycle of materials, from raw material, through use to waste disposal or recycling. To keep raw material demands to a minimum, and reduce waste disposal problems, it is necessary to plan the whole life-cycle of a product even before deciding how it should be made or what it should be made of.

Things to do

1   What else does the sewage works produce, apart from clean water? Try to think of uses for each product.

2   Name at least four types of waste, which must be removed from sewage. For each of these, describe the stage at which they are removed and how it is done.

3   Aerobic and anaerobic bacteria are used in waste water treatment. What is the difference between them? What do they do?

4   Would it help the treatment process if disinfectant was mixed with the waste water as it enters the works? Explain your answer.

5   Why is it so important to dispose of human urine and faeces so carefully?

6   Bacteria can easily break down the cellulose in discarded paper, but cannot break down polyethene. How might this affect your choice of whether to carry goods in paper or polyethene bags?

9 Recycling waste material

The Tidy Britain Group estimate that 400 000 tonnes of rubbish go into household waste bins each week. About 80% of this rubbish could be recycled but only 1% is.

Most recycled paper is stamped with a logo or description.

What waste can we recycle?

Paper

Each year the average British family throws away six trees' worth. But only 27% of the paper we use is recycled.

Recycling more paper would reduce imports and save trees.

It takes 40% less energy to produce recycled paper than to make paper from trees so it would also save energy.

It takes about 15–20 years for a tree to grow to maturity.

Glass

You and your family throw out five or six bottles or jars a week. The raw materials for making glass are sand, limestone and soda ash. These are relatively cheap and readily available. But it takes a lot of energy to convert them into glass. About 16% of glass containers are returnable – they go back to be refilled – for example milk bottles. A small proportion of non-returnable containers are recycled.

Reusing glass containers or melting and mixing broken glass with new glass saves energy.

Metal

About 8% of domestic rubbish is metal, mostly metal cans. Every household throws away about 95 kg of metal cans each year.

Many drinks cans are made of aluminium. Aluminium is non-magnetic and difficult to separate from other waste. If you test drinks cans with a magnet before throwing them away you can keep the aluminium ones separate and return them for recycling.

To produce liquid aluminium from melted cans takes 5% of the energy needed to extract aluminium from its ore, so recycling aluminium saves energy and natural resources.

Most food cans are steel. We each use about 200 steel cans every year. Like most people you probably call steel cans 'tin cans'. This is because they are coated with a thin layer of tin. Steel cans can be recycled. Because steel is magnetic, steel cans are easily extracted from other rubbish at waste treatment plants. After recovery the tin layer is removed and the steel melted down to make new steel products. 25% of every new steel can is recycled metal. Recycling steel saves energy and natural resources.

Most aluminium products are stamped with this logo.

Reusing

Before you throw something away, think twice. If it is an old bike or a toy, which you have outgrown, there may well be someone else who could make use of it. This would help to reduce some of the things we throw away.

Things to do

1   In Germany each household has several different bins, one for waste glass, one for aluminium, one for waste paper and so on. Discuss the advantages and disadvantages of such a system.

2   What is the difference between recycling and reusing? Give an example of something which is commonly reused, and something which is commonly recycled.

3   Keep a 'rubbish diary' for two weeks. Note in your diary the types and amounts of rubbish thrown away in your home. Then look at the diary and decide which items could have been recycled.

4   Create a poster, which would encourage people to reuse or recycle as much as possible.

For questions 1–4, choose the process A, B, C or D that best describes what happens.

   A breakdown by micro-organisms

   B combustion

   C photosynthesis

   D nitrogen fixation

1 The process removes carbon dioxide from the atmosphere.

2 This process is involved in treatment of sewage.

3 This process converts nitrogen gas to chemical compounds.

4 This process occurs inside petrol engines.

5 Use words from the list below to complete the paragraph.

   recycled   time   non-biodegradable
   energy   biodegradable   raw materials

Organic wastes such as vegetable peelings are _____. This means that they can be decomposed by micro-organisms. Glass and metal are _____ but they can be _____ which saves _____ and _____.

6 Study this diagram showing a cross-section through a septic tank.

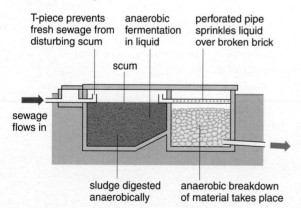

T-piece prevents fresh sewage from disturbing scum

anaerobic fermentation in liquid

perforated pipe sprinkles liquid over broken brick

scum

sewage flows in

sludge digested anaerobically

anaerobic breakdown of material takes place

   a Why is waste from some households treated in a septic tank rather than at a sewage works?

   b What role do micro-organisms play in the disposal of waste in a septic tank?

   c What would happen if large amounts of disinfectant were put down a toilet connected to a septic tank?

7 This graph gives information about what is in domestic waste.

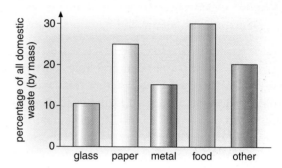

   a Which material makes up the heaviest part of the waste?

   b How much of the waste is made up of metal?

   c Give two examples of metal waste.

   d Which of the four named types of waste can be broken down by micro-organisms?

   e Which of the four named types cannot be disposed of by incineration?

8 Explain the differences between nitrogen-fixing bacteria, nitrifying bacteria and denitrifying bacteria in terns of their role in the nitrogen cycle.

9 Fast-growing trees are grown to provide wood for paper-making. Old newspapers can be used for lighting fires.
Explain how each of these processes helps to transfer carbon dioxide into or out of the atmosphere.

INTRODUCING
Staying alive

Try these first

1 List the three major groups of food.

2 State the main use of each of the food groups.

3 Explain what is meant by a 'balanced diet'.

4 Explain the role of enzymes in the digestive system.

5 The purpose of digestion is to:

   a make food taste better

   b break large molecules down into smaller molecules

   c stop us from feeling hungry.

6 When glucose is used for respiration, which of the following is NOT produced as a waste material?

   a water

   b carbon dioxide

   c urea

Plants trap energy from the Sun and store it as food, which animals eat to get energy to live.

In this unit you will learn:

- that living organisms are highly organised
- that cell membranes are *selectively permeable* and can *actively transport* molecules
- that plants are able to trap energy from the Sun through photosynthesis
- about what the products of photosynthesis are used for
- that animals use the energy trapped by plants in order to live
- about the structure and function of the digestive system
- how amylase, protease and lipase digest food
- about the difference between breathing and respiration
- about *oxygen debt* and anaerobic respiration.

Packaged food comes with a label showing dietary information and how much energy you can obtain from eating or drinking it.

1 Organisation for life

All around you, you can see examples of energy spreading out, and complex substances breaking down into simpler ones. Energy from a fire spreads out and is lost into the surroundings; new cars will eventually rust away; a dropped cup breaks, and the pieces will never 're-organise' themselves no matter how many times you throw them down. How much simpler life would be if spilt milk returned to the bottle, or jigsaws made themselves!

This pattern of 'from order to chaos' applies across the whole universe. However, if 'flying saucers' ever do come to Earth, the aliens' sensors will find all sorts of examples that seem to reverse this law. Babies grow into adults, cut skin repairs itself, and human bodies control their temperature and glucose levels by homeostasis.

Living things are often called '**organisms**', and their ability to survive depends on the use of available energy supplies to 'organise' complicated chemical changes which create living tissue. The basic structures from which living things are built up are called cells. Some very simple organisms consist just of single cells, but larger ones are made up of many different kinds of cells.

Living cells (SS) SA2, SA3

All plant and animal cells are surrounded by a sort of soft, thin cover called a **cell membrane**. The membrane is the first stage in controlling how life is organised. Membranes control what chemicals pass in or out of each cell.

Cell membranes are **selectively permeable**. They will let some molecules diffuse through into the cell, but stop some other molecules entering at all. More details of the process of **osmosis** are given in *Controlling change* (Y11).

Cell membranes can control the direction of movement of some types of molecules, and can even make them enter or leave the cell against the sort of normal diffusion gradient which drives osmosis. This process is called **active transport**, and it needs energy which is provided by respiration in the cells.

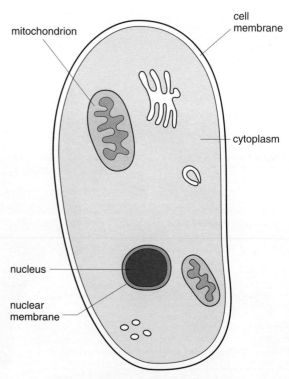

The structures in a typical animal cell.

Plant cells are different

Plant cells contain the same types of structures as animal cells, but they also have features not found in animal cells.

Tiny structures called chloroplasts are used in photosynthesis. They help plants capture energy from sunlight to drive the reactions and build up the complex chemicals needed for life from simple starting materials like carbon dioxide and water.

Animal cells do not have chloroplasts, so animals cannot photosynthesise and need to eat plants (or other animals).

Plant cells also have a structure, called the cell wall, that surrounds the membrane and provides strength.

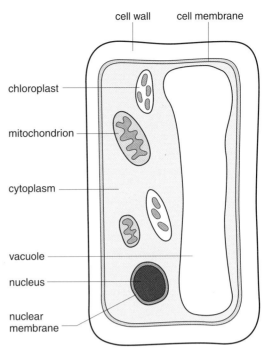

The structures in a typical plant cell.

Organisation on a larger scale

You may remember from earlier work that living organisms need certain abilities in order to survive and pass on their 'organisation' to the next generation.

Except for the smallest organisms, these tasks are made possible by having many cells of different types within the plant or animal:

- cells are organised into tissues (collections of cells all behaving in a similar way)
- tissues are organised into organs (structures with particular functions)
- organs working together make up organ systems
- many organ systems make up a whole organism (a living plant or animal).

Metabolism
Respiration
Sensitivity
Growth
Reproduction
Excretion
Nutrition

MRS GREN helps you remember the abilities a living organism requires to survive.

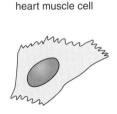
heart muscle cell

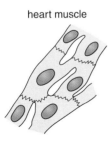
heart muscle

heart

circulation system

athlete

The levels of organisation of cells in the body make it perform well and efficiently.

? Things to do

1   Make a list of the similarities between animal cells and plant cells.

2   Make a list of the differences between animal cells and plant cells.

3   Pick an example of an animal cell and explain how it is organised into tissues, organs, organ systems, and finally, the whole organism.

2 Where does the energy come from?

Living things need a constant supply of energy to help them organise the chemical processes they depend on. All life on Earth depends on the ability of plants to trap energy from sunlight through **photosynthesis**.

Plants are energy traps (SS) SA5, SA6

Photosynthesis is the process by which plants trap energy from sunlight, combining the simple molecules of water and carbon dioxide, to make the complex organic molecule, glucose. Oxygen is also given off from the plants as a waste material (all of the oxygen in the atmosphere has come from photosynthesis). To do this chemical process, plants use the green pigment called chlorophyll. This is why all plants are green.

$$\text{water + carbon dioxide} \quad \xrightarrow[\text{chlorophyll}]{\text{light}} \quad \text{glucose + oxygen}$$

$$6H_2O + 6CO_2 \quad \rightarrow \quad C_6H_{12}O_6 + 6O_2$$

- Photosynthesis traps light energy and transfers it into chemical energy that is stored as glucose.
- The process of photosynthesis takes place in the leaf, where packets of chlorophyll (in chloroplasts) trap the sunlight energy.
- Glucose provides an energy resource for other processes in the plant. Any surplus is stored as starch.
- Photosynthesis removes carbon dioxide from the air and so helps to reduce the amount of carbon dioxide in the atmosphere.
- Photosynthesis puts oxygen into the air. This is a gas that is needed by all animals for respiration.

All the carbon in this oak tree came from the atmosphere.

Photosynthesis allows the plant to create order out of chaos and for a small acorn to grow into a majestic oak tree. A large oak tree may have a mass of over 500 tonnes which has been made out of carbon taken from the atmosphere, and water.

Green machines

Leaves are sometimes referred to as 'green machines' because they are so finely adapted to carry out photosynthesis. The leaf is light, thin, flat and contributes to an enormous surface area for trapping light energy.

The upper surface contains most of the chloroplasts for trapping light energy.

The under surface has small pores called stomata for absorbing carbon dioxide and releasing oxygen.

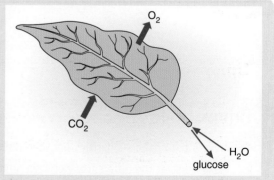

Carbon dioxide, water and sunlight are used in photosynthesis. Oxygen and glucose are made.

Leaf structure SA7-10

Chloroplasts are mainly found in the upper parts of leaves, where energy from sunlight can reach them, especially in the layer of palisade cells.

Small openings (called stomata) in the lower surface of the leaf allow carbon dioxide to enter, and oxygen and water vapour to escape.

Guard cells on either side of the stomata swell outwards when full of water, widening the opening to allow more rapid transfer of gases. In dry conditions, the guard cells relax, narrowing the openings.

Water and essential nutrients are brought to the leaf through xylem tissue in the stalk and veins of the leaf. Glucose and other products are carried to other parts of the plant through cells, called sieve tubes, that make up the phloem tissue in the veins and stalk.

Just like animals, plants also respire at all times. That is, in other parts of the plant, some of the glucose is combined with oxygen to release energy to drive essential processes.

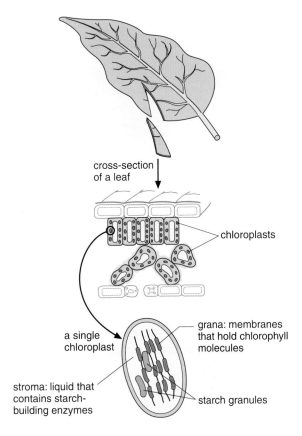

The leaf is a very organised and highly adapted organ.

At night, when respiration is still going on, but photosynthesis isn't, plants use oxygen, and release carbon dioxide. During the day, photosynthesis is more rapid than respiration, and on balance, the plant takes in carbon dioxide and releases oxygen.

Some glucose molecules are polymerised (linked together) to form cellulose, which provides strength for cell walls, and some is used to make other chemicals. For example, the plant will have absorbed nitrogen through its roots in the form of nitrates. The nitrates will enable the plant to first make amino acids, then join the amino acids together in different combinations, to make all the different types of protein that the plant requires for growth.

The plant can store surplus glucose by converting it into starch, another polymer of glucose. It is this fact – that plants produce more food than they need by photosynthesis – that enables humans and other animals to survive on planet Earth.

? Things to do

1   Carbon dioxide is a greenhouse gas.
    Explain how plants help to reduce the levels of carbon dioxide in the atmosphere.

2   The tropical rainforests are sometimes called the 'lungs of the world'.
    Explain what this means.

3   It is sometimes said that plants give out oxygen during the day, and use it up at night.
    Explain why this is an over-simplification.

There are several factors that can limit the rate of photosynthesis and so affect how fast or well a plant grows. The most important limiting factors are light, carbon dioxide and temperature.

Light

Light intensity has the most noticeable effect. For example, photosynthesis occurs rapidly during the day but stops all together when it gets dark at night. The brighter the day, the faster photosynthesis occurs and thus the greatest rate of photosynthesis usually occurs round about mid-day when the sun is at its brightest. Plants grow towards the light to get as much light energy as possible.

The rate of photosynthesis in a plant ...

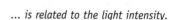

... is related to the light intensity.

Carbon dioxide

However, there comes a point at which no matter how bright it is, photosynthesis cannot go any faster. You can see from the graph that the rate levels off. This is because another limiting factor, such as carbon dioxide, is now restricting the rate of the reaction.

The normal concentration of carbon dioxide in the atmosphere is about 0.04%. If this level were to rise higher then the rate of photosynthesis would increase even more.

Look at the second graph. You can see that as the light intensity increases, so does the rate of photosynthesis. However it soon reaches its maximum or optimum level. The rate can then only be increased by raising the level of carbon dioxide even higher. The rate then increases to a higher level but reaches its optimum once more.

Eventually, increasing the levels of carbon dioxide would have no further effect on the rate of reaction. That would be because a new limiting factor had been reached, such as temperature.

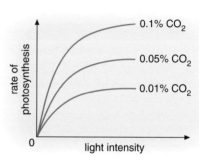

It also depends on the amount of carbon dioxide available ...

Temperature

Temperature as a limiting factor has a rather different effect. All chemical reactions get faster as the temperature rises, because collisions between particles become more energetic. However, for enzyme catalysed reactions, if the temperature rises much above normal, the collisions begin to alter the shape of the enzyme. It becomes denatured and stops working. Thus, increase in temperature at first makes photosynthesis faster, but beyond a certain temperature, the rate falls off rapidly and finally stops.

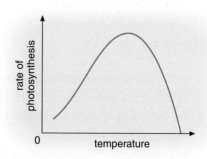

... and on the surrounding temperature.

Controlling these factors to increase food production

Farmers can use this knowledge of limiting factors to increase the yield of some of their crops. This is especially true for crops that are produced in greenhouses, where the environment can be carefully controlled.

Light intensity, temperature and even levels of carbon dioxide, can be increased to improve the rate at which plants photosynthesise and grow. This means that growing time is reduced, the growing season is extended and farmers can often plant an extra crop, thus increasing the efficiency of the greenhouse.

A greenhouse provides an environment in which conditions can be controlled.

Things to do

1   A piece of pondweed was placed in water at a temperature of 15 °C in a dark room, and lit using a lamp. The light intensity and the rate of photosynthesis were measured with the lamp at different distances away. These results were obtained.

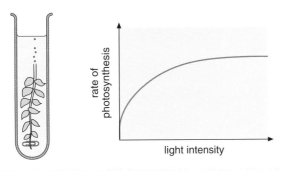

   a   Suggest what might be measured to compare the rates of photosynthesis.

   b   Copy the graph and draw an extra line on it, to show what you think would happen if the temperature was increased from 15 °C to 20 °C.

   c   Suggest what would happen to the rate of photosynthesis if carbon dioxide was bubbled through the water.

   d   Explain what would happen to the rate of photosynthesis if the temperature was raised to 60 °C.

2   Most plants lose their leaves in the winter. Suggest why this happens.

Animals need energy

Animals, as well as plants, need supplies of energy for body processes. The energy which animals need comes from complex organic chemicals such as fats, proteins and carbohydrates which they get from eating plants (or other animals!). Thus, as you saw in *Balancing acts* (Y10), the sunlight captured by photosynthesis is the source of all the energy flowing through food chains and food webs.

How animals manage to use this energy supply is the next chapter in the story.

Sunlight is the source of all our energy.

Food glorious food

Perhaps the best way to see how animals deal with food is to look at how we as humans do it. Although there are differences from animal to animal, the basic process is the same for all animals.

Digestion (SS) SA11

Digestion is all about taking in large complex molecules, by eating plants and other animals, and breaking them down into smaller, soluble molecules.

These smaller molecules can be absorbed through the gut wall and into the blood stream.

It is only when these small molecules get into our blood stream, that we can use them for growth by the release of the energy that they contain.

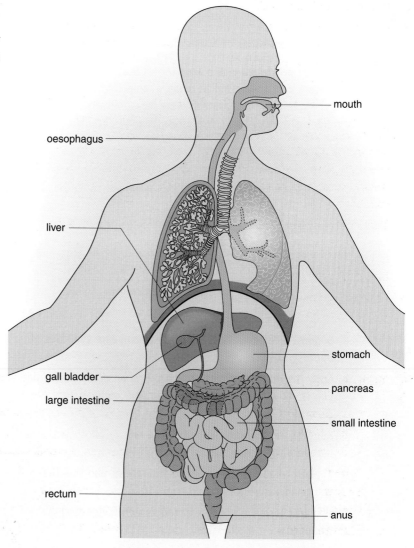

The main organs involved in digestion are shown here. This is called the digestive system.

These are some of the main stages in digestion:

- Food is taken into the mouth, chewed and broken down into small pieces. It is mixed with saliva that lubricates the food enabling us to swallow. The saliva contains the enzyme amylase for breaking down carbohydrates.

- The food is pushed by waves of muscular contraction, called peristalsis, down the oesophagus and into the stomach.

- Once in the stomach, the food is mixed with acid and the enzyme protease to start the breakdown of large protein molecules into smaller amino acids. The stomach acid also kills any bacteria on the food, thus making food poisoning less likely.

- When the food has been in the stomach for several hours, it is reduced into a creamy paste that is squeezed through into the small intestine. The small intestine is in fact very long, but is small in diameter. It is in the small intestine that the food is mixed with other digestive juices that continue with the breakdown of the food.

- One of these juices is from the pancreas. This contains other enzymes such as lipase for breaking down fat, amylase for breaking down carbohydrate and more protease for breaking down more protein.

- Bile is also added from the gall bladder. This does not contain enzymes, but instead emulsifies the fats by separating the large lumps into tiny droplets. This increases the surface area of the fats and makes it easier for lipase to break them down. (You use detergents in the same way to emulsify fat when you wash dishes. Emulsions of this type contain drops of oil which are so small they mix into water.)

- The food is now squeezed along the small intestine, which is about five metres long. The enzymes continue to break down the food and the small soluble molecules are absorbed into the blood stream.

- In the large intestine, which is only about two metres long, water is absorbed and the waste material is eventually eliminated from the rectum, through the anus.

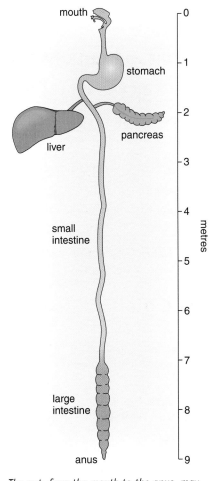

The gut, from the mouth to the anus, may be up to nine metres long.

? Things to do

1. A textbook says "If there were no plants, there wouldn't be any animals either." Explain what this means.

2. State what the process of digestion does to the large molecules found in food.

3. Enzymes are sometimes called organic catalysts. Explain what this means.

4. State two reasons why the stomach has such a low pH.

How food gets squeezed along

 SA12, SA13

Food moves along the gut by a process that is similar to the way that toothpaste is squeezed out of a toothpaste tube.

This process of squeezing food along the gut is called **peristalsis**.

It is a result of circular muscle around the gut contracting, in a wave that passes along the gut.

It normally takes at least 24 hours, and often longer, for the food to be pushed from the mouth to the anus. This gives plenty of time for the enzymes to break down the food into small soluble molecules.

There are three main groups of enzymes involved in digestion:

- ones that break down carbohydrate: for example, amylase
- ones that break down protein: protease
- ones that break down fats: lipase

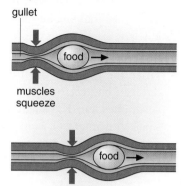

 There are three major types of food substance: proteins, fats and carbohydrates. During your lessons you will learn how to test for each of these in foods.

Food substance (large, insoluble molecules)	Type of enzyme	Digested to form small soluble molecules
Starch (a carbohydrate)	amylase and other enzymes break down starch into simple sugars	glucose (a simple sugar)
Protein	protease breaks down protein into amino acids	amino acids
Fats and oils	bile (not an enzyme) spreads fats into tiny droplets to give a bigger surface lipase breaks fat into fatty acids and glycerol	glycerol fatty acids

 Amino acids, simple sugars, fatty acids, and glycerol, are all small soluble molecules that can be absorbed through the gut wall and into the blood stream. They are called the products of digestion.

How small soluble molecules are absorbed (SS) SA14

The small soluble molecules of digested food pass through the wall of the small intestine and into your blood stream. This process of absorption takes place as the food passes along your **small intestine**.

This part of your digestive system is called 'small' because it is narrow. However, to allow time for all the useful products of digestion to be absorbed, it is very long – about 5 metres!

Although the small intestine is very long, the surface area for absorption needs to be made even larger.

This is done by having an inner lining to the small intestine which has a very folded surface. The surface area is increased even further by having small finger-like projections called villi, which are on this folded surface.

Each villus is supplied with a blood vessel so that the small molecules can easily diffuse through the surface of the villus and into the blood.

The next section of the gut is called the large intestine. Here water is absorbed into the blood, and solid waste collects ready for excretion.

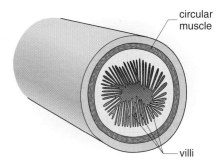

The surface area of the inside of the small intestine is much more than that of the smoooth outer wall.

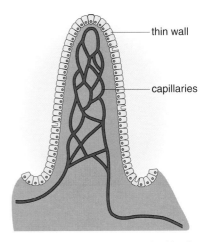

The inside of a villus showing the blood vessels.

? Things to do

1 Make a list of the features of the small intestine which help to make it more efficient for absorbing the products of digestion.

2 Explain why many different enzymes are needed in the digestive system.

3 Bile makes fats or oils form an emulsion with the water in the gut. List some other examples of emulsions. What is important about the size of the particles in an emulsion?

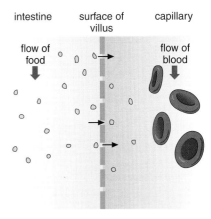

Small molecules pass through the wall of the villus into the blood in the capillary.

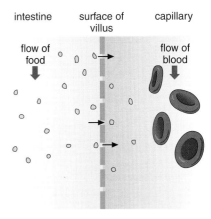

You have seen in this unit how plants are able to trap the energy from sunlight. They then store surplus energy as chemical fuels that we call food. Animals are able to access this available energy supply, by eating this food and digesting it. The last chapter in the story is how the animals are able to release this energy in a safe way so that they too can use it to organise themselves into complex structures.

Food as a chemical fuel (SS) SA15

The energy which plants store is released by animals through a process that is the opposite to the process of photosynthesis. This process is called **aerobic respiration** (it is called this because it needs oxygen, which you get from the air). The equation that describes it is the exact opposite of the equation for photosynthesis. Indeed an easy way to remember it is to write the equation for photosynthesis backwards.

glucose + oxygen $\rightarrow$ carbon dioxide + water + ENERGY

$$C_6H_{12}O_6 + 6O_2 \rightarrow 6CO_2 + 6H_2O + \text{ENERGY}$$

Aerobic respiration works by combining glucose with oxygen. This process is like the one for burning. Burning glucose on a fire would mean combining the glucose with oxygen to release carbon dioxide and water. The end result of aerobic respiration is exactly the same as if the glucose had been burned! Fortunately, this doesn't mean that every time we eat some food we will burn up in flames and smoke!

The difference between respiration and burning is that respiration is controlled by enzymes. This means that the energy is released in small amounts and not in one big rush. The gradual release of this energy explains why you can keep your body temperature at 37 °C even though this is often warmer than your surroundings.

Fortunately, respiration is not quite the same as burning!

Where does respiration happen?

Glucose comes from digestion in the gut, oxygen is taken in through the lungs (see *Sports science*, Y11). Both of these are carried in the blood to all the cells in the body.

Each cell is never more than the width of one cell away from a small blood vessel (capillary) and glucose and oxygen can diffuse from the blood vessel across this small distance to each and every cell.

The waste material from respiration, carbon dioxide, dissolves in the blood and is carried back to the lungs to be breathed out.

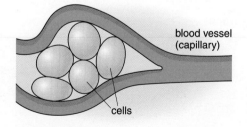

Capillaries taking blood to cells in the body.

Mitochondria – the powerhouses of cells (SS) SA16, SA17

The chemistry of respiration takes place inside structures called mitochondria that are found inside the cell.

The inside surface of a mitochondrion is highly folded (to increase surface area) and it is on this surface that the chemical reactions to release the energy in glucose take place.

The reaction takes place in many steps, each catalysed by different enzymes. Enzymes are also needed to break down harmful by-products of the reaction, such as hydrogen peroxide, which would otherwise damage the cell.

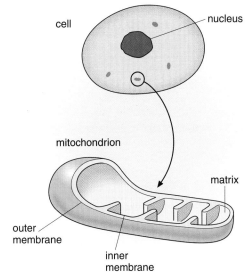

Mitochondria are sometimes referred to as the 'powerhouses' inside a cell.

Respiration and breathing – not the same!

This type of respiration is often referred to as **cellular respiration** to avoid confusion with 'breathing', which some people also call respiration.

It is much safer to only use the term respiration when referring to the process of energy release inside the mitochondria.

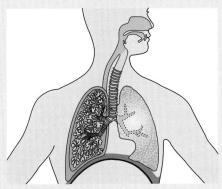

Lungs are used for breathing.

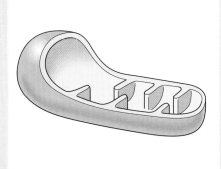

Mitochondria in cells are used for respiration.

? Things to do

1. Explain the differences between photosynthesis and respiration.
2. Explain why burning releases energy very quickly but respiration releases the same energy very slowly.
3. Explain why body temperature at 37 °C is almost always warmer than the surrounding air.
4. Explain the differences between breathing and respiration.
5. Suggest why mitochondria are sometimes called the cell's 'powerhouses'.
6. Explain how the structure of a mitochondrion helps it carry out its function.
7. Explain the role of the blood in supplying the cell with glucose and oxygen and in carrying away the waste products.

Plants respire too!

Plants only use sunlight directly for photosynthesis, but they need to maintain other vital processes to stay alive.

Some of the glucose that is made by photosynthesis is transported in sap through phloem tubes to all parts of the plant. There, cellular respiration in mitochondria in the plant cells breaks down the glucose, just as in animal cells, to release energy.

So, respiration is going on all the time in plants, but during daylight the rate of photosynthesis is so much faster that we don't notice the effect of respiration.

Throughout both night and day, plants use a little oxygen and make a little carbon dioxide. In daylight only, they use a lot of carbon dioxide and make a lot of oxygen.

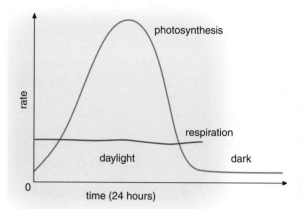

Graph showing comparative rates of photosynthesis and respiration over a 24-hour period.

Respiration without oxygen

When you need energy fast (for running a race, for example) the mitochondria respire as fast as possible. Oxygen is used up faster than the blood can supply it. The level of dissolved oxygen in the cells falls and a second, less efficient type of respiration begins in the cytoplasm of the cell.

This anaerobic (without air) respiration converts glucose to lactic acid and provides some extra energy. Unfortunately, this cannot go on for long, since lactic acid causes pain and muscle fatigue.

The energy obtained is less than half that from aerobic respiration, because the glucose is not completely broken down.

Even after you stop running, you go on panting and your pulse takes time to return to normal. The exercise has removed much of the dissolved oxygen normally in the cells.

Until this 'oxygen debt' is paid back, you go on panting. At the same time, the blood carries lactic acid away to be dealt with by the liver.

Panting continues after you finish running to restore the oxygen levels in your blood.

Anaerobic bacteria and fungi

Some bacteria and fungi like yeast can also respire anaerobically.

However, instead of making lactic acid like humans do, they produce alcohol instead. If we respired like bacteria, we would become drunk just by running. You can just imagine what school sports day would look like!

$$C_6H_{12}O_6 \rightarrow 2C_2H_6O + 2CO_2 + ENERGY$$

When yeast does this we call it **fermentation** and we use the process for making wine and beer. Yeast only does this when there is no oxygen available, so it is most important that the process takes place in a vessel fitted with an air lock to keep out the oxygen in the air, but to let out the carbon dioxide produced by anaerobic respiration.

This brewing kit shows how air does not get into the vessel where fermentation is taking place.

The final chapter

This unit started by explaining how living organisms use energy from the Sun to 'organise' themselves through growth. The energy is trapped by plants and stored as food that animals can then use as their energy source. The final transfer of energy in this story, is that most of the energy ends up as heat radiated away from the bodies of living organisms. However, in the process the energy has been used to allow all the complex diversity of living organisms that we see on this planet, to grow and thrive. Life is truly an amazing process.

Things to do

1 Some people think that plants should be removed from hospital rooms at night. Suggest what might make them think this.

2 Explain why anaerobic respiration would not be a good idea to use all of the time.

3 Suggest why yeast makes alcohol by anaerobic respiration, but animals do not.

1 Answer each part of this question using words from this list of things found in living cells:
**cell wall   cell membrane   nucleus
vacuole   chloroplast   cytoplasm
mitochondrion**

   a Which of these things are found in both plant and animal cells?
   b Which are found only in plant cells?
   c Write short notes to describe the function of each of the things in the list.

2 a List the seven different types of function that might show that an object is a living organism.
   b Which of these is shown by:
      **a human baby   a cloud   a wood fire
      a motor car**

   For each of these, explain whether you would classify it as a living organism.

3 This diagram shows a cross-section of part of a leaf. Leaves carry out photosynthesis.

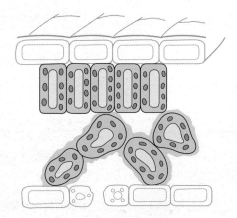

   a Copy the diagram and label palisade cells and a stomata.
   b i What raw materials are taken in by the leaf for photosynthesis?
      ii What waste product of photosynthesis is given out from the leaf?
      iii Write a balanced equation for photosynthesis.
      iv Explain how the amount of water available to the plant can control the rate of photosynthesis.

4 Bobby runs to keep fit. His leg muscles ache if he runs too fast.

   a Normally, Bobby's muscle cells release energy by aerobic respiration of glucose. Write a word equation for this reaction.

   When Bobby runs fast, his muscles also respire anaerobically.

   b What is anaerobic respiration?
   c Give two disadvantages of anaerobic respiration.
   d After Bobby stops running, he continues to pant for a while. Explain why.

5 This diagram shows some parts of the digestive system.

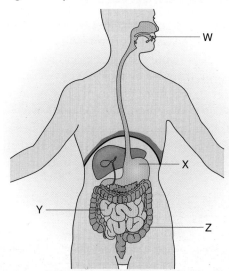

   Name each of the parts W, X, Y and Z, and describe the job done by each of them.

6 The label on a beefburger shows that it contains 12% protein, 30% fat, 5% carbohydrate and 5% fibre. The rest of the mass is made up of water.
   a What is the function of protein in the diet?
   b What is the main function of carbohydrate in the diet?
   c How would you test for the presence of:
      i starch
      ii simple sugars
      iii protein
      in a sample of food?
   d What is formed from protein during digestion?

INTRODUCING

The Earth in space

Try these first

1 There are _____ planets in the solar system. How many can you name?
2 The Sun is a _____ which is one of billions in a g_____ called the _____ _____ .
3 The time taken for the Earth to spin once on its axis is _____ .
4 The time taken for the Earth to complete one orbit of the Sun is called a _____ .
5 A _____ is a satellite which orbits a planet.
6 Asteroids are pieces of rock orbiting between _____ and _____ .

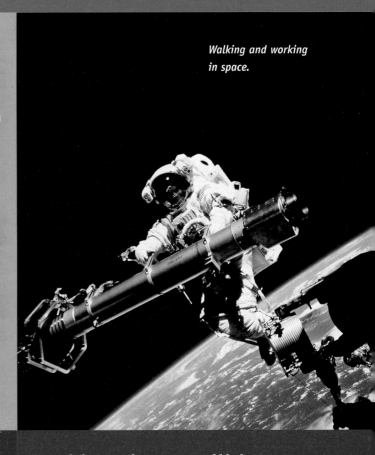

Walking and working in space.

The sky at night.

In this unit you will learn:

- about galaxies, stars, planets and moons
- the distances to planets and their sizes
- how stars and planets were formed and what might happen to them
- what it is that fuels the Sun
- how gravity holds the Universe together
- the big bang theory, some other ideas of creation, and how they fit what we observe
- how rockets work
- different orbits for satellites and what we use them for
- how we might look for other life in the Universe.

1 Ideas about space

This unit will build on work you have done in earlier lessons about stars and planets.

Stars (SS) ES1, ES2

Our Sun is a **star**. Stars are powered by nuclear reactions. The middle is very hot – about 15 000 000 °C in the Sun. The surface is much cooler – about 6000 °C for the Sun. Stars give out light and often other radiation.

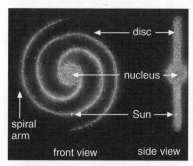

This drawing of our spiral galaxy shows the approximate position of the Sun.

Galaxies

Galaxies are made from huge numbers of stars. Our Sun is in a galaxy that we call the Milky Way. On a clear night you can see a bright band of stars in a big arch across the sky. This is the Milky Way and there are huge numbers of stars in this direction. The Milky Way is a flat spiral galaxy and the Sun is about a third of the way in along one of the arms.

Some galaxies are attracted together by gravity and form clusters. The Milky Way is in a cluster called the Local Group which has about 20 galaxies.

Note the spiral structure of this galaxy.

Clusters of galaxies

The **Universe** is the collection of all the galaxies of stars and the time and space that they are in.

Planets

Planets are fairly large objects that orbit round a star. Planets don't give out light. We see them by the light that they reflect from the star. A planet will get most of its energy by radiation from the star. A planet closer to the star will receive more energy and will have a higher temperature than a planet farther away.

We are always trying to find out more about the planets and our knowledge is always changing. A lot of information comes from satellites that can look at the planets without our atmosphere getting in the way.

The expanse of sea on Earth speckled with land masses is clearly visible from space.

The planets, in order of their distance from the Sun are:

Mercury, Venus, Earth, Mars, Jupiter, Saturn, Uranus, Neptune and Pluto.

Pluto's orbit is less circular than those of the other planets and it can sometimes be closer to the Sun than Neptune.

The Earth is just the right size and distance from the Sun to have an atmosphere and an average surface temperature at which water is liquid. Its crust contains carbon, which can form many different compounds, including those that life depends on.

Scientists are looking for other planets that might support life.

We now know that there are planets round some of the stars and we are trying to find out more about them.

Moons

Moons are made from the same materials as planets and seem to have been formed at about the same time. We can only see them by the light that they reflect. Instead of going into their own orbit round the Sun, each moon orbits a planet. Some planets in the Solar System have a lot of moons – Saturn has about 20 – some have none. The Earth has just one Moon.

Meteors

Meteors are smaller pieces of rock. If they hit the atmosphere of the Earth they will usually burn up and we see them as shooting stars. If a piece is big enough to reach the ground it is called a meteorite.

Comets

Comets come from outside the Solar System but may become trapped into very big orbits by the Sun's gravity. The core will be a few kilometres across and made from dust and ice. Some of the material forms a tail pointing away from the Sun that might be thousands of kilometres long. The reflected light as a comet nears the Sun can make it look very bright in the sky.

The Moon has a rocky surface with craters (dark patches) made by meteorites.

Shooting stars can be seen on clear cloudless night skies.

The Comet Hale-Bopp with a tail that's clearly visible. In 1997 it made its closest flyby to Earth since 2000 BC.

?

Things to do

1 Look at the data about the planets on the following pages. Make a bar chart to show the temperature of each planet.

   a What is the general trend as distance from the Sun increases?

   b Which planet doesn't fit this pattern? Try to find out why this is.

2 Use the information about the planets to make a computer database. Search the database to find:

   a Which planet has the most moons?

   b Which planet has the shortest day?

   c Which planet has the longest year?

What are the planets like? (SS) ES3

We have good pictures from probes that have been sent out past the other planets and their moons. We can work out the mass and density of the planets from the time taken for an orbit of the Sun. This gives a picture of the planets and their composition but they are all a long way away and more evidence is being collected all the time.

The first four planets are 'rocky' planets. They have lost light gases such as hydrogen from their atmospheres because of their high temperature. They are dense and contain metal ores and a hot core.

Planets farther out are cold and icy and bigger than the inner planets. They have kept hydrogen and helium and chemicals such as liquid ammonia. The amount of metals and rocky material is much smaller. Pluto (the outermost planet) doesn't fit this pattern and may have been captured as it came close to the Solar System.

Venus
Composition: rocky
Distance from the Sun (AU): 0.72
Orbital period: 224 days
Rotation period: 243 days
Surface gravity: 0.90
Number of moons: 0
Average surface temperature: 726 K
Diameter: 12 104 km

Mercury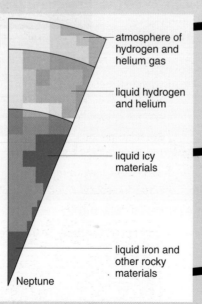
Composition: rocky
Distance from the Sun (AU): 0.39
Orbital period: 88 days
Rotation period: 59 days
Surface gravity: 0.38
Number of moons: 0
Average surface temperature: 452 K
Diameter: 4878 km

Jupiter
Composition: icy
Distance from the Sun (AU): 5.20
Orbital period: 12 years
Rotation period: 10 hours
Surface gravity: 2.7
Number of moons: 18
Average surface temperature: 125 K
Diameter: 142 800 km

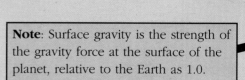

- atmosphere of hydrogen and helium gas
- solid mantle of silicates (compounds of silicon, oxygen and metals)
- liquid hydrogen and helium
- liquid icy materials
- solid iron core
- liquid iron and other rocky materials

Mercury

Neptune

These 'wedges' of Mercury and Neptune show the composition of these planets.

Note: Surface gravity is the strength of the gravity force at the surface of the planet, relative to the Earth as 1.0.

Pluto

Composition: uncertain
Distance from the Sun (AU): 39.53
Orbital period: 248 years
Rotation period: 6 hours
Surface gravity: 0.5
Number of moons: 1
Average surface temperature: 37 K
Diameter: 2300 km

Earth

Composition: rocky
Distance from the Sun (AU): 1
Orbital period: 365 days
Rotation period: 24 hours
Surface gravity: 1.0
Number of moons: 1
Average surface temperature: 289 K
Diameter: 12 756 km

Neptune

Composition: icy
Distance from the Sun (AU): 30.06
Orbital period: 165 years
Rotation period: 22 hours
Surface gravity: 1.2
Number of moons: 8
Average surface temperature: 48 K
Diameter: 49 528 km

Mars

Composition: rocky
Distance from the Sun (AU): 1.52
Orbital period: 2 years
Rotation period: 24 hours
Surface gravity: 0.38
Number of moons: 2
Average surface temperature: 200 K
Diameter: 6787 km

Saturn

Composition: icy
Distance from the Sun (AU): 9.54
Orbital period: 12 years
Rotation period: 10 hours
Surface gravity: 1.2
Number of moons: 18
Average surface temperature: 163 K
Diameter: 120 660 km

Uranus

Composition: icy
Distance from the Sun (AU): 19.18
Orbital period: 84 years
Rotation period: 18 hours
Surface gravity: 0.8
Number of moons: 18
Average surface temperature: 60 K
Diameter: 51 118 km

Forming stars and planets ES4

The theory of planet formation which best fits the facts as we know them is based on ideas from Immanuel Kant (1724–1804) and some later work by Pierre-Simon de Laplace (1749–1827).

It begins with ice and dust and gas rotating in space held together by gravity. We can see objects like this, called **nebula**, at other places in our galaxy. Most of this was hydrogen and helium but there were some heavier elements such as iron that were probably left from the explosion of an earlier star.

Gravity slowly attracted these particles together and as they joined and grew bigger they attracted each other more and more strongly.

There was most matter near the centre and gravity pulled it together to make a **star**. This is how our Sun was made.

At the same time gravity pulled the material into a flat rotating disc.

The centre of the disc was hotter and most of the icy particles in the inner part of the disc were vaporised. This left the rocky dust as the main material in the inner part of the disc. As the Sun began to shine a stream of hot, fast moving gas called the Solar wind blew out from it and carried the icy material outwards in the disc where it was collected by the growing outer planets.

More collisions formed the planets as we see them now. Moons were objects that came close enough to a planet to be captured in an orbit by gravity, without colliding.

All of this took about 10 million years and the planets all ended up orbiting round the Sun, with the inner planets having mostly rock material and the larger outer planets being icy gas giants.

Choosing between theories

Several other theories have been suggested to explain how the planets were formed. One popular theory was that at some time in the past the Sun collided with a comet. The planets were the result of lumps of material thrown out by the force of the collision. Another theory is that the gravtitational attraction of another star that passed nearby may have pulled material off the Sun and this cooled to form the planets.

These pictures show the sequence of events in the theory of Kant and Laplace for the beginning of the Solar System.

Both of these theories could account for the formation and position of the planets, but once astronomers began to collect information about what planets are made off, these theories were discarded, because they cannot explain why outer planets generally have a different composition to inner planets. As new methods make new evidence available, theories may have to be modified, or even abandoned altogether, if they do not match up with the new evidence.

Measuring distances in astronomy

Just south of the city of York a disused railway line has been turned into a cycle path. Along this path are models of the Sun, Earth and other planets. The model of the Sun is 2.4 metres in diameter. The Earth is just over 200 metres away, and Pluto is over 10 kilometres away, near the village of Riccall! The University of York website on the Internet gives information about the model and about the Solar System.

Our Solar System is only a tiny part of the Universe, but even so it is very large.

In order to give simpler numbers to work with, astronomers use a unit called the astronomical unit (AU). One AU is the average distance from the Sun to the Earth (149.6 million kilometres).

This 2.4 metres Sun is part of a scale model Solar System which stretches 10 kilometres from York to Riccall.

Table of statistics for planets in the Solar System.

Planet	Distance from the Sun (AU)	Density (gcm^{-3})
Mercury	0.39	5.43
Venus	0.72	5.24
Earth	1.00	5.52
Mars	1.52	3.93
Jupiter	5.20	1.32
Saturn	9.54	0.70
Uranus	19.18	1.27
Neptune	30.06	1.77
Pluto	39.53	–

? Things to do

1   Which are the rocky planets?
2   Which are the icy planets?
3   Why do the inner planets now contain little icy material?
4   Why was the original atmosphere of hydrogen and helium lost from Earth?

What is mass?

Mass is the measure of how much material (matter) an object is made of. The mass of an object is always the same, wherever it goes.

The mass of an object is important if you want to change its speed or direction. The force needed to change the movement of an object is found by multiplying the mass by the acceleration:

Force = mass × acceleration

$F = ma$

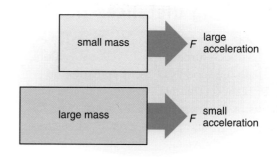

Gravity and matter

Gravity is a force that attracts objects towards each other. It acts on every object. The bigger the object, the stronger its gravitational attraction. The further apart two objects are, the weaker the force between them. Objects such as stars and planets are so large that the force can be felt over huge distances.

What is weight?

When an object is close enough to a planet or a moon it will be attracted to it by gravity and we call that force **weight**. In your case the mass of your body is attracted by the Earth and your weight is the force of gravity towards the centre of the Earth.

On the surface of the Earth each 1 kilogram (kg) of mass will be attracted towards the Earth by a force of approximately 10 newtons (N). We say that the strength of the Earth's gravitational field is 10 N/kg.

The weight of an object depends on where it is. The Moon is smaller than the Earth and it has less mass so the strength of its gravitational field at the surface is smaller, only 1.6 N/kg.

Weight = mass × g

(g = gravitational field strength)

An astronaut would need to use the same force to accelerate a loaded trolley on the Moon as on Earth – the **mass** is the same, wherever you are.

But the astronaut would find it much easier to pick up the load on the Moon, because its weight (the downward gravitational force) is smaller.

The mass of an object is the same on the Earth as on the Moon but the weight of an object is heavier on Earth.

Air resistance and terminal velocity

Imagine dropping a large stone and a small stone. The force of gravity is proportional to the mass of each stone, so they should both fall together, with the same acceleration. If you also drop a feather (smaller mass and smaller weight) would it fall at the same rate as the stones?

Astronauts did this on the surface of the Moon by dropping a falcon feather (the Moon-lander module was called *Falcon*) and a hammer. The two fell exactly together.

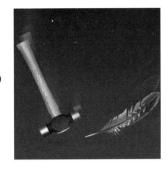

The feather and hammer test.

However, on Earth, in the air, the feather is much slower than the hammer – there are other forces at work!

The difference is caused by the extra force of air resistance.

Air resistance is a counter force that gets bigger the faster you move through the air or if it acts on a larger area. When you drop the feather it soon reaches a speed where the air resistance pushing upwards is as big as its downward weight. When the forces balance the feather will travel at constant speed – it has reached **terminal velocity**.

The comparison between a hammer and feather falling on the Moon and a hammer and feather falling in air on Earth.

If you pedal your bike as hard as you can you will reach a terminal velocity when the air resistance becomes equal and opposite to the forward force that you make. Many plant seeds use this idea to stay in the air for longer and get as far from the parent plant as possible – think how this might work for dandelion seeds or sycamore seeds.

? Things to do

1   On Earth, $g = 10$ N/kg   on the Moon, $g = 1.6$ N/kg.
    What is the weight on the Moon and on Earth, of
    a   a 70 kg woman
    b   a 900 kg buggy
    c   a 0.5 kg ball
    d   a 0.1 g feather?

2   Explain why:
    a   a hammer and a feather fall at the same speed on the Moon, but different speeds in Earth's atmosphere
    b   the hammer falls more slowly on the Moon than on Earth?

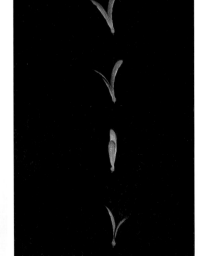

Lime seed 'spinners' can stay in the air for a long time because the force of the air resistance is the same as the force of weight.

5 Rockets and orbits

Escaping from gravity

Newton noticed that forces come in pairs. If object A exerts a force on object B then object B also exerts a force on object A, but in the opposite direction. If you fire a gun the bullet goes forward but an equal and opposite force (the recoil) sends the gun backwards. This is Newton's third law.

This equal and opposite force is used to power a rocket motor. Fuel is burnt and is pushed out of the back of the rocket at high speed. The force pushing the motor forward is then the same size as the force pushing the fuel back.

Since the motor doesn't need anything else to push against it will work quite well in space.

The rocket must carry with it all the fuel and oxygen that it needs to burn. Look at the picture of the shuttle to see its large fuel tanks for the booster rockets.

To take off and get a rocket into space the engines must exert a very large force. The rocket has to reach a speed of 11 kilometres per second or gravity will pull it back to Earth. Scientists can work out the forces that are needed by using Newton's second law:

$$F = ma$$

The calculation is made a little more complicated because the fuel load, which must also be lifted, is getting smaller all the time as it is burned so the same force makes an increasing acceleration.

Once the spacecraft is in space, far from the Earth, it will keep going at the same velocity without the engine running and the engine will only be needed for changes of direction or speed.

Staying in orbit

Rockets are also used to put satellites or space stations into orbit round the Earth. These have not escaped from the Earth's gravity and it is their weight that actually pulls them towards the Earth and keeps them in orbit.

Newton imagined a projectile being fired from the top of a high tower. If it is fired slowly it will not

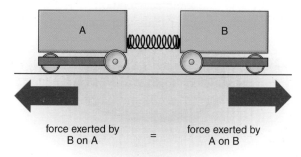

force exerted by
B on A   =   force exerted by
A on B

trolleys recoiling from a spring

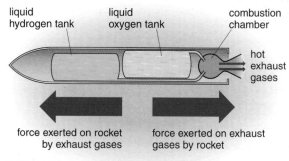

liquid hydrogen tank   liquid oxygen tank   combustion chamber

hot exhaust gases

force exerted on rocket by exhaust gases   force exerted on exhaust gases by rocket

rocket motor

Two examples of Newton's third law in action.

The space shuttle at take-off requires huge amounts of energy from burning fuel to overcome the force of gravity.

get far before it hits the ground. If it is fired faster then it will still be pulled to the ground in the same time but will go further before it lands.

This assumes that the ground is flat. If you had a very high tower and a very fast projectile then, as it falls towards the Earth the surface is also curving away beneath it.

Newton realised that there must be a speed at which the falling projectile would just be matched by the curvature of the Earth. It would then go right round the Earth in a curved path and become a satellite.

A real satellite is above the atmosphere. It will not have air resistance to slow it down and it can stay in orbit for a long time.

Going round in circles (SS) ES8

A satellite is one example of things moving in a circle. In order to push something into a curved path, there must always be a sideways force. This is called **centripetal force**. The size of the force depends on the radius and the speed of the object as well as its mass.

Imagine whirling a block tied to a string round your head. The inward force is provided by the tension in the string. If the string breaks the block will no longer have a centripetal force and will fly off in a straight line.

On this fairground ride, as the people move in an arc, the centripetal force is provided by the rails pushing inwards. They feel the seats push against them and might imagine that they are being pushed out against the seat.

Gravity produces the centripetal force which keeps moons and satellites in orbit round their planets and keeps planets in orbit round the Sun. As the shuttle or a space station orbits the Earth it is its weight towards the Earth that acts as the centripetal force.

Things to do

1   A fairground attraction shows Wayne and Phil riding a motorbike around the inside of a metal sphere.

Explain how the centripetal force is produced.

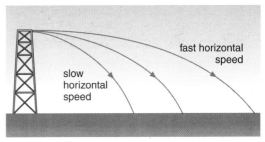

Speed makes a difference to where a projectile lands.

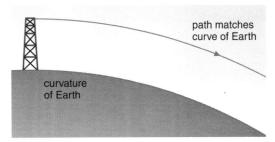

There is a speed at which a projectile can travel so that it orbits the Earth rather than falls to Earth.

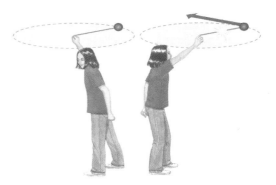

If you swing a ball round and the string breaks, it will fly off in a straight line.

Use is made of the centripetal force in adventure rides and in space flight.

The Law of Gravity

People have studied the movement of the planets for hundreds of years. In 1619, Johannes Kepler described the link between the radius of the orbit of a planet and the time it took to go once round the orbit. However, he was unable to explain the pattern he had found. About 60 years later, Newton developed a theory of gravity based on the idea that the force of attraction between two bodies varies inversely as the square of the distance between them. Newton was able to calculate orbits of planets that agreed with Kepler's law. It often happens in science that careful observation can reveal patterns of behaviour before any explanation has been found.

Isaac Newton developed the universal law of gravitation, supposedly after considering why apples fall to the ground!

Gravity is a universal force. Each particle of matter, whether large or small, attracts all other matter towards it. Newton recognised two aspects of this.

The force F of attraction between two objects increases as their masses (m_1, m_2) increase.

The force is inversely proportional to the square of the distance (d) between the centres of the objects:

$$F = \frac{G \times m_1 \times m_2}{d^2}$$

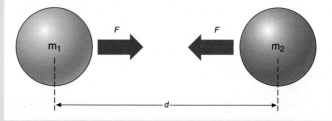

There is gravitational attraction between any two bodies.

In the case of objects on the surface of the Earth, m_1 (the mass of the Earth), d (the radius of the Earth) and G (a constant) are all fixed. The equation can be written as:

$$F = m \times g$$

On the surface of the Earth, g is approximately equal to 10 Newtons per kilogram.

The gravitational pull of any object decreases with distance. So the strength of the Earth's gravity gets less as you move away from the centre of the Earth (for calculations involving gravity, it is simplest to assume that all the mass of an object is concentrated at its centre of mass).

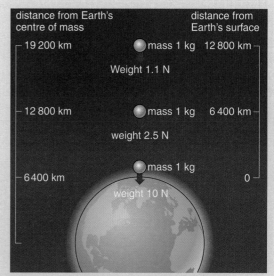

Height has an effect on a body's weight.

? Things to do

1 How far above the surface of the Earth would the 1 kg mass have a weight of 0.4 N?

Round or over? ES9, ES10

There are two main types of orbit into which we put satellites.

In 1947 Arthur C Clark, also known as a science fiction writer, worked out how satellites in orbit round the Earth could be used to communicate from one side of the world to the other. A satellite placed in an orbit above the equator with a radius of 42 100 km would take 24 hours to complete one orbit. Since the Earth is rotating at this same speed the satellite would appear to be stationary when seen from Earth.

An orbit like this is called a **geostationary orbit**.

A satellite like this can be used to send TV pictures down to a large part of the surface of the Earth. Communications from one side of the Earth to the other can be made by sending the signal up to one satellite, across the orbit to another satellite and then down again.

Alternatively, some other satellites orbit by passing over the poles. In a **polar orbit** the rotation of the Earth will mean that the satellite passes over a different strip of the Earth on each orbit. Satellites in polar orbit are ideal for weather observation, military planning, mapping or looking at the state of crops.

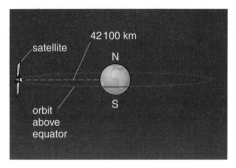

A satellite in geostationary orbit.

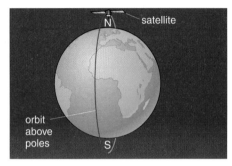

A satellite in polar orbit.

Things to do

2   For each of the following say how the centripetal force is provided:
   a   a motorcyclist going round a bend
   b   a bucket of water whirled at arm's length without spilling the water
   c   a passenger on a fairground ride that 'loops the loop'
   d   the Earth going round the Sun.

3   Look at the satellite TV dishes close to your home.
   It is likely that all the satellite dishes will face the same way. Why is that?

4   A friend sees a rocket on Guy Fawkes night. Explain to him how it works and why it doesn't need to push against the ground.

5   a   How long does a geostationary satellite take to complete one orbit?

   b   A geostationary orbit has a radius of 42 100 km. What is the circumference of the orbit?

   c   How fast is a satellite travelling in a geostationary orbit?

6   Find out about the following satellites – when were they launched, what are they for and what sort of orbit you think each is in?
   a   INTELSAT   b   METEOSAT   c   ASTRA   d   GPS

7   The picture shows a part of the Earth as seen from a satellite. What useful information can we get from pictures like these?

7 Dark lines in the starlight

Remember the spectrum?

You will already have seen how to produce a spectrum. The spectrum from a filament bulb is a continuous spectrum which contains all the colours from red to violet.

It is caused by having a lot of atoms very close together and giving them a lot of energy. The red light has longer waves and carries less energy than the blue light at the other end of the spectrum.

You can use a prism to see all the colours that make white light.

Line spectra

Spectra can also be obtained by heating gases, where the atoms are far apart. In this case the atoms will produce their own individual pattern of separate coloured lines. The atoms of each different element produce a different pattern of lines.

If you look at the spectrum from a sodium lamp through a pocket spectrometer, the light is all in two yellow lines that are very close together – there are no other visible colours.

The presence of particular lines can be used to identify the elements that emit the light. If there is a mixture then the proportions of each element can be found from the brightness of the lines.

The line spectrum for helium.

The line spectrum for sodium.

Absorption spectra

Atoms are good at emitting the light in their own special set of colours. They are also good at absorbing exactly the same frequencies. If a continuous spectrum is sent through a gas then the atoms will absorb their own particular colours so that the spectrum has a corresponding set of dark lines. This is called an absorption spectrum.

In 1802 William Wollaston noticed that the light from the Sun had dark lines across it. In 1814 Joseph von Fraunhofer realised that these lines were an absorption spectrum. The Sun emits a continuous spectrum which passes through the cooler gases above the surface. These absorb their own frequencies and the dark lines help astronomers to identify the elements that the Sun is made from. From this we can tell that the Sun is mostly hydrogen, with about 25% helium and 2% of other elements.

A hand-held direct vision spectroscope is a good way to look at the line spectrum of an element.

The absorption spectrum of sunlight, showing Fraunhofer lines.

? Things to do

1   Try drawing some stars on the surface of a balloon. As you blow it up all the stars will get farther apart as the surface expands but none of them are at the centre. From **each** one all the others would seem to be getting farther away.

Shifting to the red

The spectrum from other stars has the same pattern of lines but they are not in the place you would expect – they are all shifted towards the red end of the spectrum.

The elements can still be identified from the pattern of the lines but what causes the shift in wavelength?

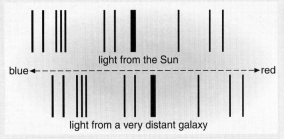

The shift in wavelength observed when comparing the absorption spectra of the stars with the Sun.

The Doppler effect

Think about what you would hear if you are standing by the side of a railway line and a train passes.

As the source of sound approaches you the pitch of the sound seems higher. As the source leaves you the pitch becomes lower. The effect is bigger if the source moves faster. Johann Doppler first described this effect in 1842 and it is called the Doppler effect. The Doppler effect works with light waves as well as with sound.

Think about the light moving towards you from a star. If the star is moving away from you as the light is emitted the waves are spread out over a greater distance – they have a longer wavelength.

A longer wavelength corresponds to a lower frequency and a redder colour. Stars or galaxies that have their light shifted towards the red must be moving away from us. This explains why the absorption spectrum seems to be moved and also enables astronomers to work out how fast stars and galaxies are moving.

An expanding Universe

When astronomers look at the light from other stars and galaxies they find that they are all moving away from us, the shift is always to the red. This seems to show that the Universe is expanding and that all the galaxies are moving away from each other.

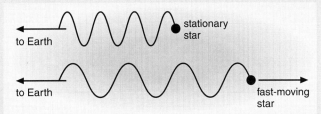

The difference in the absorption spectra is explained by the theory that the stars of the galaxies are moving away from us.

? Things to do

2   An astronomer plots a graph of the spectrum from a distant star and gets the following result. A little later some students are to visit her lab and she wants to show them the spectrum to illustrate her work.
Write some notes for her so that she can give explanations of the following:
a a continuous spectrum   **b** a line spectrum
c the dark lines in an absorption spectrum

3   The students compare the results with a spectrum from hydrogen on Earth. They find that some of the lines in the star spectrum are in the same pattern but seem to have been moved towards the longer wavelength end of the spectrum. What two facts can they learn from this?

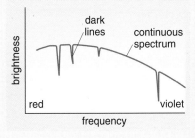

Over the centuries, there have been many theories to explain the behaviour of the stars. Even today, there are still disagreements about the history of the Universe.

The Big Bang theory

This theory assumes that all the matter in the Universe came from one great explosion. At first, the material would be travelling out quickly and become evenly spread. As it cooled, gravity would pull it into the clusters which form nebulae and finally stars. A 'big bang' like this would have sent out lots of radiation, and astronomers believe that the 'background radiation' they have found in all directions in the Universe is the remains of this.

Gravity would slow down the spread of matter. Light from very distant stars has taken a very long time to reach us, so we see them as they were then. More distant stars do seem to be moving away more quickly than nearer stars.

The steady state theory

This different theory says that the Universe is always expanding steadily and new matter is always coming into existence. The new matter fills gaps so that the Universe keeps its present appearance. However, this theory cannot explain the presence of 'background radiation'

A star is born (SS) ES12

As you saw on page 104, gravity can pull together gas and dust in space to form rotating discs. As more and more material is pulled in its temperature rises. Much of the material at the centre is hydrogen. Eventually, the temperature and pressure become so great that nuclei of hydrogen atoms are squashed together forming helium atoms. This **nuclear fusion reaction** releases enormous amounts of energy. The dense ball of matter has become a main sequence star. The reaction will continue, until the supply of hydrogen starts to run out.

A main sequence star in the Crab nebula.

Red giants

When most of the hydrogen fuel in a star has been used up, it begins to cool, becomes redder, and the outer part expands. The star becomes a **red giant**. Because the core is producing less energy, gravity makes the star collapse inwards. The density increases until other fusion reactions can start, turning helium nuclei into elements such as carbon.

Different endings

What happens next depends on the size of the star. Stars about the size of our Sun lose much of their outer material which is thrown out into space. The core cools, leaving a **white dwarf**, just a dim remnant of the former star.

More massive stars end differently. A star with mass about ten times that of the Sun will have a core that continues to get hotter and will eventually form heavier elements such as oxygen, neon, sulphur and eventually iron.

The iron nuclei can't be fused to produce more energy and the core then collapses again causing the star to explode as a **supernova**. For a very short time – about a month – the star is a brilliant object in space, brighter than a whole galaxy. This is throwing out heavier elements that will be included in future stars and planets. The core that is left will cool to form a **neutron star** that we might be able to detect as a pulsar that emits regular bursts of radio waves. A really massive star may make a core so heavy that not even light can escape and it becomes a **black hole**.

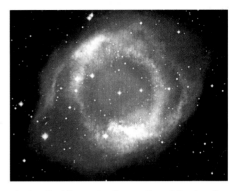

A star shedding outer layers: the white dwarf star forming at the centre.

Supernova 1987

Pictures taken before and during the explosion of Supernova 1987.

Things to do

1   Write a brief summary of what is meant by the Big Bang theory and how it explains the facts described in this chapter.
2   What is meant by red shift? What does this shift tell us about the Universe?
3   The following terms describe the steps in a scientific process. Put them in the correct order.
    Develop a theory.
    Make careful observations.
    Make new observations.
    Modify the theory if necessary.
    Make a prediction based on the theory.
4   Make a list of the names of the stages that a star can pass through. Display these stages as a flow diagram.
    (Hint: it will branch at some stages.)
5   Use the Internet to find pictures to illustrate your flow chart.

What can we look for?

The only life forms we have discovered so far need carbon and water to build the complicated molecules that life depends on. A lot of research has been done in looking for signs of these basics on the planets of our Solar System, including landings on the Moon, Venus and Mars. Water has been found in some places. Organic chemicals (those based on carbon) seem to be relatively common – on the surface of the moons of Mars for example. The most likely possibility is Mars where it would have been warmer and wetter 2 or 3 billion years ago.

The surface of Mars showing a loading ramp for a robot vehicle.

Where else can we look?

The first step is to make sure that other star systems do have planets. It is only in the last few years that planets or stars with dust discs for planet formation have actually been detected. Such stars seem to change slightly in position or in brightness as the planets orbit between the star and us.

Having found that other planets exist we still cannot examine them as we can those in our own solar system. One of our best rockets would take about 60 000 years to reach the nearest other star system, Alpha Centauri, so landings and fly-bys are not practical.

What else can we look for?

If we assume that there is not only life but that it is also intelligent we might look for radio or light transmissions.

Astronomers first began searching star systems for artificial radio transmissions in about 1960. The scientists in the Phoenix Project look for narrow bands of radio transmission coming from nearby Sun-like stars. The scientists use very large radio telescopes in Australia and Puerto Rico. Those stars that are thought to have planets have already been included in the survey. A new array of telescopes called the Allen Telescope Array is due to look at many more stars from a site in California.

The Arecibo radio telescope in Puerto Rico is 305 metres in diameter.

Find out what is meant by the *Drake Equation* and what it might tell us about extraterrestrial intelligent life.

Looking for laser light coming from other stars would assume that an intelligent life form is sending a beam in our direction. A search for laser light is being done. It has the advantage of being less liable to interference and false alarms.

So far all of these searches have found nothing that is definitely extraterrestrial – but they will keep on looking!

Sending a reply

The searches that we have looked at are passive searches – they look and listen but don't reply and are not sending out messages.

Most researchers have not been very interested in sending out messages – apart from not knowing which direction to choose, the time one would have to wait for a reply is a problem. If you sent a message to a star system 100 light years away then you would have to wait 200 years for a reply!

The Owens Valley Telescope is used for detecting radio transmissions.

Some messages have been sent out from Earth. In 1974 a message from the Arecibo telescope in Puerto Rico described our Solar System, compounds important for life, the structure of DNA and the shape of a human. It was sent towards the galaxy M13 about 25 000 light years away.

? Things to do

1 If there is intelligent life in M13, how long might we have to wait for a reply to the message that scientists sent out?
2 If a signal was received do you think we should try to reply. If we did reply what sort of information might extraterrestrials understand?
3 Most large telescopes are sited at the top of mountains or in places with a very low population. Explain why this is an advantage.
4 What is special about the chemistry of carbon that leads us to think that its compounds are so important for life?
5 How might we first know that a planet is orbiting a star outside the Solar System?

This telescope is used for sending messages to outer space.

The flight of *Apollo 11* is probably the most famous space flight ever. It was the mission that first landed a person on the Moon. Some of the most important stages on the journey are shown here:

1 Lift-off from Cape Canaveral. Enormous first stage rockets were required here to provide sufficient thrust to lift the rocket against the pull of the Earth's gravity.

2 Once the craft was away from the Earth's surface the first stage was no longer required. It separated from the rest of the craft and was abandoned.

3 At this point the craft was moving around the Earth. With no air resistance to slow it down, the craft kept a constant speed. The effect of the Earth's gravity was to keep the craft in orbit.

15 ... to splash down in the Pacific Ocean.

4 To move away from the orbit around the Earth the craft required a force. This was provided by igniting the engine at a point calculated to send the craft towards the Moon.

14 Moving more slowly the command module spiralled down towards the Earth ...

13 At this point all of the craft apart from the command module was abandoned.

Things to do

1 Make a list of headings for each stage of the *Apollo 11* flight. Arrange these headings in sequence to make a flow diagram.

2 Beside each stage on your flow diagram, write a short note describing the size of the force exerted by *Apollo 11*'s rocket motors at this stage. Use words like large, small, no force, and so on.

3 Choose one point where the force exerted by the rocket motors was large. Explain why a large force was needed at this point. Choose another point where the force exerted by the rocket motors was small, or zero. Explain why only a small force or no force was needed at this point.

4 At one point on both the outward and the return journey, the gravitational pull of the Earth on the spacecraft was exactly balanced by the gravitational pull of the Moon. Draw a sketch diagram and mark on it roughly where you think this point would be. Explain the reasons for your answer. Would it be true to say that, at this point, the spacecraft was in a region of zero gravitational field?

5 The lunar module has much less powerful motors than the Saturn rockets which lifted *Apollo 11* off the Earth. It is also much less streamlined in shape than the Saturn rocket. Explain why the lunar module could be designed in this way.

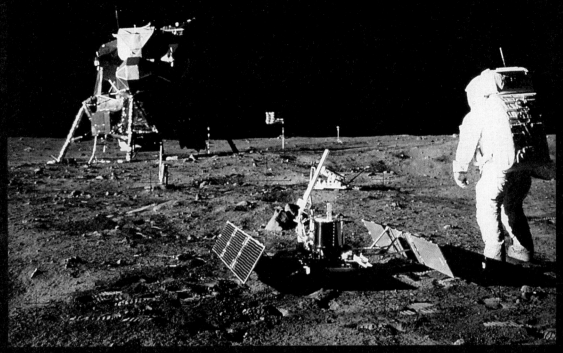

This is Buzz Aldrin, a crew member of Apollo 11, setting up some equipment on the Moon's surface. His fellow crew member Neil Amstrong was the first person to set foot on the Moon (1969). The third crew member, Michael Collins, remained in the orbiting command module.

5 Once on course for the Moon the engine was only required to change direction.

6 When the craft was close to the Moon, the Moon's gravity kept the craft in orbit, at a constant speed.

7 Here the lunar module separated from the rest of the craft. Moving slowly, the lunar module began to spiral down towards the Moon.

8 The lunar module's engine was switched on in reverse. The thrust from the engine was sufficient to slow the descent to the Moon, but not enough to overcome the gravitational attraction.

9 Landing! The astronauts spent $21\frac{1}{2}$ hours on the surface of the Moon.

12 Once on course for the Earth, the engine was only required to change direction.

10 Take-off from the Moon. The lunar module's engines now had to provide sufficient thrust to lift it off the Moon. A much smaller force was required than on Earth, because the Moon's gravity is six times weaker.

11 The lunar module rejoined the command module. Crew and equipment were transferred to the command module. To move away from orbit around the Moon required a force. This was provided by igniting the engine at a point calculated to take the craft towards the Earth.

1 Place the following in order, smallest first:

Universe, comet, planet, moon, star, galaxy, meteor

2 Which is the largest planet?

    a   Which planet is remarkable for the rings around it?

    b   Which planet has an atmosphere that raises its temperature far above what we would otherwise expect?

3 What is meant by a main sequence star? What is its next stage likely to be?

4 What is a supernova? How long would it last and what might be left behind afterwards?

5 Which chemicals are thought to be essential for the evolution of life?

6 What signs might an astronomer look for if he was looking at a star for signs of a planet orbiting round it?

7 One theory about the creation and evolution of the Universe is called the Big Bang theory. Write a short description of the theory for a friend of your age who has not heard about it.

8 The space shuttle uses booster rockets to produce the huge force needed at launch. The thrust of a rocket can be obtained from:

Thrust (N) = speed of exhaust (m/s) × mass of fuel used per second (Kg/s)

    a The solid rocket boosters each burn fuel at a rate of 4200 kg/s. What is the speed of the exhaust?

    b The shuttle engines produce exhaust gases with a speed of 3650 m/s. How many kilograms of fuel is burned by the engines each second?

    c Use your answer to **b** to work out how long it takes to burn all the fuel in the external fuel tank.

    d Use the information in the diagram to work out the total weight of the shuttle at the moment of launch.

    e Use the information in the diagram to work out the total thrust of all the engines.

    f Use your answers to questions **d** and **e** to work out the net upward force on the shuttle as it begins take-off.

    g Use the information in the diagram below to find the total mass of the shuttle and then use your answer to question **f** to work out its acceleration.

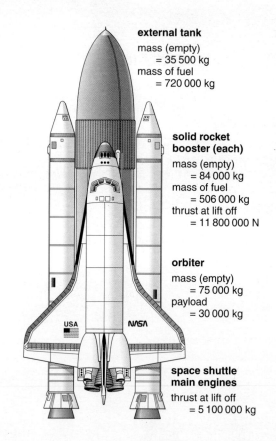

external tank
mass (empty)
= 35 500 kg
mass of fuel
= 720 000 kg

solid rocket booster (each)
mass (empty)
= 84 000 kg
mass of fuel
= 506 000 kg
thrust at lift off
= 11 800 000 N

orbiter
mass (empty)
= 75 000 kg
payload
= 30 000 kg

USA   NASA

space shuttle main engines
thrust at lift off
= 5 100 000 kg

INTRODUCING

Evolution

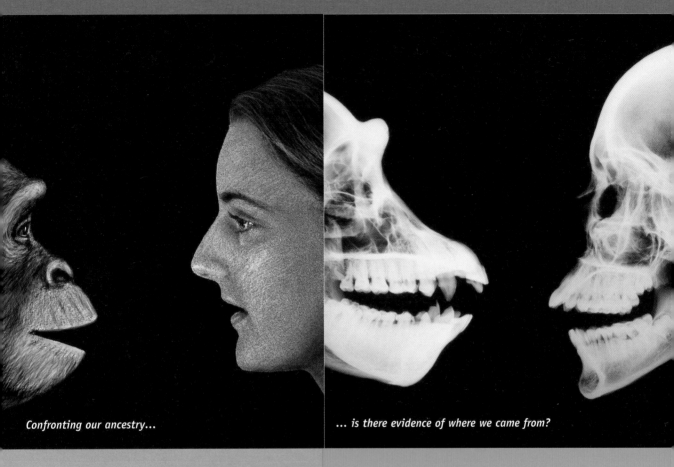

Confronting our ancestry...

... is there evidence of where we came from?

Try these first

1   Look at the two following descriptions about variation. One of them describes environmental variation. The other describes genetic variation. Decide which is which.

   a   When Bobby returned from holiday, he noticed that his skin was more tanned than his friend's skin, who had stayed at home.

   b   Bobby had blue eyes, just like his grand-mother's.

2   State which of the following is not an example of selective breeding.

   a   breeding from the cows that produce the most milk

   b   letting domestic cats escape and breed in the wild

   c   allowing the hens that produce the most eggs to breed with the cockerel

   d   breeding a dog to be entered for a dog show.

In this unit you will learn:

- how variation can arise from a combination of genes and the environment
- that sexual reproduction is a source of variation
- that mutation is a source of variation
- how sex is determined
- how characteristics are inherited
- about genetic engineering
- that the fossil record is evidence for evolution
- how variation and selection may lead to evolution or extinction.

'All change' on planet Earth

If you have ever looked at old films on TV, you will soon have realised that the way we live is very different now to 50 years ago. Living things are changing too. The story of life on our planet is all about how things change.

You will already have learnt that some of the differences between individuals may be due to how we inherit **genes** from our parents, while others may be due to how our environment affects us. Sometimes, it may be due to a mixture of both. We call these differences **variation.**

The naturalist Charles Darwin (1809–1882) who developed the modern theory of evolution.

Types of variation		
environmental	**genetic**	**mixture of both**
scar tissue	eye colour	height
tattoos	blood group	weight
length of hair	tongue rolling	intelligence

Evolution (SS) EV1–7

Evolution is the story of how species change over long periods of time. People used to think that life had always existed just as it did in their day. They never considered that life had changed and believed that God had placed all life on the Earth just as it is now.

Charles Darwin worked on board a ship called the *HMS Beagle* which sailed around the world from 1831–36. He studied and collected plants and animals from all the places that the ship visited. He soon realised four things:

- Organisms produce far more offspring than can ever grow up to survive. Most die young.
- Population numbers remain fairly constant for year after year.
- Sexual reproduction produces offspring that are slightly different from their parents. We call these differences variation.
- Characteristics inherited from parents are passed on from generation to generation.

It was from these four basic facts that Darwin produced his ***Theory of Evolution***:

- All offspring produced by sexual reproduction are slightly different from their parents.
- If the environment changes (hotter, colder, wetter, drier and so on) the new conditions will not favour all the organisms that live there.
- However, because all the organisms are slightly different, some may be better suited to the new conditions.
- Individuals that are better suited to the environment will survive better and produce more offspring.

This process will be repeated, generation after generation. It is called **natural selection**. Changes in the environment will change which individuals survive.

Canada geese with a brood of chicks, not all of which will survive.

These kittens are slightly different from each other and from their mother.

Fossil evidence for evolution

Some of the main pieces of evidence for evolution come from the fossil record. That is to say from remains of plants and animals which have become embedded in sedimentary rock. The original shape of the organisms is preserved in the rock.

Fossils are important because:

- they are the preserved remains of dead organisms that lived millions of years ago.

- using modern scientific methods, the fossils can be dated. By looking at lots of fossils and dating them, it gives us a picture of how animals and plants have slowly changed over a long period of time.

- fossils are surrounded by soil and rocks that tell us what conditions were like at the time. This enables us to see how the organisms were adapted to live in their surroundings. By linking the ages of fossils to the conditions at the time when the plants or animals were alive, scientists can see how, when the environment has changed, organisms have evolved to live in the new, changed environment.

Artist's impression of ammonites and other ancient creatures swimming in the sea.

Analysis by radioisotope dating can indicate the age of the fossil and the conditions in which it lived.

Ammonite fossils are clearly visible in this sedimentary rock from the Jurassic period, approximately 150 million years ago.

Things to do

1 Use the ideas mentioned above to explain how the giraffe got its long neck.

2 Imagine you are Charles Darwin. Write a page from your diary to explain what it was like to have a new theory that was disapproved of by so many people.

3 Use the Internet to find out about a man called Wallace and the role he played in the *Theory of Evolution*.

2 Variation and the gene pool

SS EV8

The characteristics that you inherit are decided by a set of instructions present in the nucleus of every cell. Each section of these instructions is called a **gene**. Natural selection can happen most easily when the population of a species includes many different versions of genes, to provide a large amount of variation. This ensures that at least some individuals will survive changes in conditions to maintain the species. The variety of different genes available in a population is called the **gene pool**.

Have cheetahs enough variation in the gene pool to adapt to dramatic changes in the environment?

An example of a small gene pool can be found in cheetahs. Scientists think that thousands of years ago the cheetah nearly became extinct. Because only a few were left, the gene pool became very small. When conditions improved and the cheetah started to breed more numbers, the genes available were few in number.

Although there are more cheetahs around today, they all have similar genes and therefore little variation. If the environment were to change again, the cheetahs might lack the genes needed to adapt to the new conditions.

Extinction is forever

Scientists think that the main reason animals and plants become extinct is because the environment changes and the organisms cannot adapt to the new conditions. This can happen for two reasons:

- The animal's gene pool is too small to provide sufficient variation for the organism to evolve.

- Sometimes changes are so great or rapid that the species lacks the genetic variation, or cannot breed fast enough to evolve to the new conditions. The dinosaurs may have been wiped out by the impact of an asteroid with Earth, changing the conditions instantly and not giving time for the dinosaurs to evolve.

The impact of asteroids falling on Earth would have been huge.

Evolution – the evidence

Evolution is still referred to as a theory because it cannot be proven. The only way to prove it would be to invent a time machine and go back in time and have a look.

However, there is a large amount of evidence that supports the theory. In law, people can be sent to prison based on what is called circumstantial evidence. This means that the evidence does not *prove* the guilt of the accused person and a jury must decide whether the evidence is overwhelming enough to pass a guilty sentence.

The evidence for evolution could be regarded as circumstantial. However, it is overwhelming ...

Evolution in action

Normally evolution takes millions of years to happen. However, some organisms reproduce so quickly that evolution happens in a short period of time.

Unlike humans, who only produce a new generation roughly every 20 years, bacteria can produce a new generation every *20 minutes*. This is about half a million times faster than humans. So evolution that would take 1 000 000 years in humans can happen in two years in bacteria.

This is how bacteria are able to evolve resistance to many of our antibiotics.

In a population of bacteria, a few will have a genetic make-up which is resistant to a particular antibiotic.

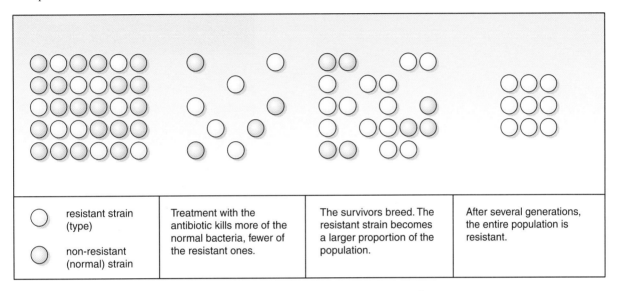

○ resistant strain (type) ○ non-resistant (normal) strain	Treatment with the antibiotic kills more of the normal bacteria, fewer of the resistant ones.	The survivors breed. The resistant strain becomes a larger proportion of the population.	After several generations, the entire population is resistant.

A less resistant strain of bacteria is removed by successive treatment with antibiotics, leaving a resistant strain. This is why it is important to complete any course of antibiotics, so that all of the bacteria are killed. If any survive, they will be the most resistant ones, and will pass this resistance on.

The way in which individuals can vary is explained later in this chapter. It is the variation that is present in a population which allows it to survive any change in its living conditions. Some individuals in a population will possess the particular gene that helps them to survive change. Thus, they survive and breed, so that the characteristic becomes more widespread throughout the population of the species. This is natural selection at work.

? Things to do

1   Make a list of as many differences as you can think of between yourself and a friend.
    Produce a table of three columns with headings 'environmental', 'genetic' and 'mixture of both' and place the differences you have thought of in the correct column.

2   Francis Galton was a scientist who thought that all intelligence was inherited and that schools and upbringing had nothing to do with it. What do you think?

EV

Variation and the gene pool

125

3 Asexual and sexual reproduction

Asexual (without sex) reproduction occurs when there is only one parent. The new plant or animal is an exact genetic copy of the parent, with all of the same genes, and no others. There are several different ways in which this can happen.

Splitting into two

Some single-celled microscopic organisms living in ponds reproduce by just splitting into two. Each cell makes an identical copy of itself when it divides.

Growing runners

Some plants, such as strawberries, grow shoots or runners that have baby plants growing on them.

When the baby plant grows its own roots, the shoot from the parent rots away and a new plant has been formed.

Both of these examples produce individuals that are identical copies of their parents. Individuals that are genetically identical are called 'clones'.

This means that organisms that reproduce by asexual reproduction never change. Each generation is identical to the one that went before it. Later in this unit, you will find out how changes can happen in genetic material, but it is a very slow process. Species which are limited to only asexual reproduction find it difficult to adapt to changes in their environment.

Plant breeders make use of asexual reproduction when they take 'cuttings' of plants. A small shoot is cut off, carrying just a few leaves. If this is planted, it can be grown into a complete new plant. The process is helped by dipping the lower end of the cutting into a solution containing a hormone that promotes root formation.

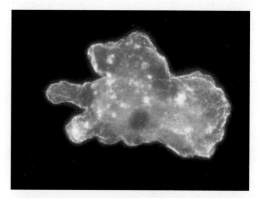

An amoeba in the process of dividing and forming an identical copy of itself.

A strawberry plant with runners which are rooting in the surrounding soil.

Just imagine what it would be like if humans reproduced in this way and everyone looked the same as everyone else!

A cutting being taken from a geranium plant in a pot.

The cutting being planted in a new pot.

The parent plant and new plant.

Genes and alleles

Chromosomes occur in pairs. The 46 chromosomes in a human cell are made up of 23 homologous pairs. 'Homologous' means 'of the same type'. With only one exception, if the two chromosomes that make up a pair are compared, they contain the same sequence of genes (cells like this are said to be diploid: 'di' means 'two').

How does this help? It means that we have two copies of every gene, one on each of the pair of chromosomes. Each of these single copies is called an allele. In many cases, the two alleles will both be exactly the same. However, it is possible for alleles to have different structures and behave in different ways.

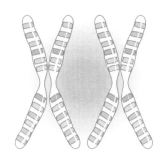

A pair of homologous chromosomes with a matching sequence of genes.

For example, one gene controls the ability to 'roll' your tongue. Two different versions of this gene exist in the human population. One allele develops tongue-rolling, the other doesn't. If both your alleles (one in each chromosome) are for tongue-rolling, you will be good at this trick. If both are for 'not-tongue-rolling', you won't be able to do it. Tongue-rolling is not a very important trick to help you survive! However, it does illustrate the principle.

In each pair of chromosomes in your cells, one has come from your mother, the other from your father. Each parent has contributed half of the total of information that makes up 'you'. In this way, different alleles can be mixed and spread amongst a population.

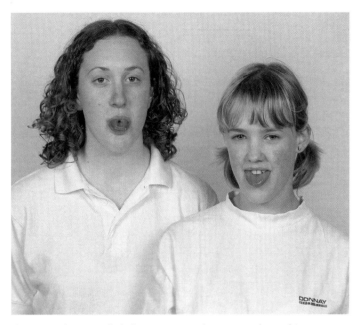

Someone who can roll their tongue ... and someone who can't!

Mixing genes together

The mixing of genes from two parents is called sexual reproduction. The offspring will inherit half of its genetic information from the mother, and half from the father. In each of the 23 pairs of chromosomes in a human baby, one has come from the father, one from the mother.

In order to allow this mixing, special cells called gametes must be produced by each parent. In humans, males produce sperm, and females produce ova.

These cells contain only half the usual number of chromosomes. They are called haploid cells (remember *h* for *h*alf the usual number!). Each gamete contains just one from each of the pairs of chromosomes in a normal cell.

Sexual reproduction creates new combinations of alleles, and allows alleles for successful characteristics to spread through a population.

It's clear that these are members of the same family. They have characteristics in common.

4 Copying cells

Before cell division

The process by which one living cell divides to produce two identical copies of itself is called **mitosis**. This process happens in asexual reproduction, and in growth and repair of tissues.

The 'instructions' which control chemical processes in a cell are stored on tiny strands called **chromosomes** (most human cells contain 46 chromosomes, but other species may have different numbers of chromosomes).

Before cell division, each chromosome produces an exact copy of itself. The two copies remain joined, and can be seen as X-shapes just before cell division.

Cell copying: mitosis

The 'copies' separate. Each new cell receives one copy of every chromosome. New cell membranes and nuclear membranes grow to complete the two new cells. Each cell has a complete set of 'genetic instructions' which is an exact copy of the original.

Each chromosome is made up of a large number of shorter sections called genes. Each gene provides the instructions for one process or feature of activity in the cell. The copying of all the chromosomes into each new cell means that each one has a complete set of instructions for all the processes it may need to carry out.

Preparation for cell division

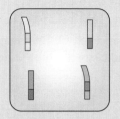

This cell contains two homologous pairs of chromosomes. One allele on each is shaded. Note that the chromosomes in each pair contain different alleles.

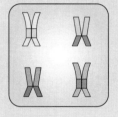

Before cell division, each chromosome is copied. (The two copies remain joined together.)

The membrane round the nucleus dissolves away, allowing the chromosomes to line up across the centre of the cell.

mitosis

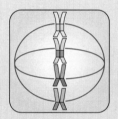

chromosomes form one line down the centre of the cell

meiosis

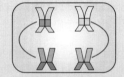

homologous pairs line up side-by-side

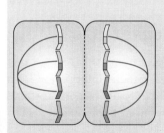

one copy of each chromosome goes to each new cell

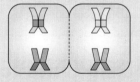

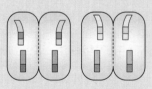

members of each homologous pair are separated, then the copies split to produce four cells, each containing half the original number of chromosomes

---

?

Things to do

1   A 'map' of how genes are arranged in human chromosomes is called a **genome**. Look up genome on the Internet and try to find out how many genes are needed to carry the instructions for a human being.

Cell division: meiosis EV9

Gametes are formed by a special type of cell division called **meiosis**. The chromosomes are duplicated ready for cell division, just as for mitosis, but they line up in pairs. At the first stage of division, one from each homologous pair goes to each new cell. These cells immediately divide again, forming a total of four new cells. Each new cell contains just *half* the original number of chromosomes. In men, this happens in the testicles, producing sperm. In women, it happens in the ovaries producing ova.

Each person generates large numbers of gamete cells, but they will not all contain the same mixture of alleles. When chromosomes are divided during meiosis, it is purely random which one of each pair goes to which gamete cell.

A new individual is created when an ovum is fertilised by a sperm. The two nuclei are joined, making up a full set of 46 chromosomes. In each pair, one has come from the father, and one from the mother.

Each offspring will inherit some characteristics from each of its parents, but because of the random way chromosomes divide during meiosis, children in the same family may each inherit a different combination of characteristics.

Although children in the same family share many characteristics, each will have inherited a slightly different combination of alleles from their parents.

The only exception to this rule is when identical twins are born. One ovum is fertilised by one sperm in the usual way, but as the **zygote** (fertilised egg) begins to divide, two cells become completely separated and each grows into a separate **fetus**.

This means that identical twins each inherit exactly the same set of alleles.

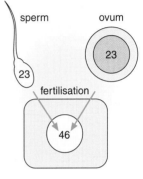

A sperm and ovum combine to form a zygote with 46 chromosomes.

Things to do

2 Explain why identical twins can be thought of as clones.

3 Suggest why some people think that studying identical twins may help to decide the variations caused by inheritance and those caused by the environment.

4 In plants, the gamete cells are the ova and pollen grains. If a plant has 24 chromosomes in its leaf cells, what would be the haploid number in its pollen cells?

5 Explain why it is necessary for gamete cells to contain only half the usual number of chromosomes.

Many studies of identical twins have been made to try to find out how much variation between them can be linked to differences in lifestyle and environment, rather than inheritance.

5 Inheritance

The same or different? (SS) EV10

A baby inherits two alleles for each gene – one from the mother, one from the father. Sometimes both alleles will be the same. Sometimes they will be different. What happens then?

For example, an allele responsible for fur colour in guinea-pigs has two different forms, one for black, one for brown. If a guinea-pig has two 'black fur' alleles, then the fur will be black. Two 'brown fur' alleles give a brown coat. However, if a guinea-pig inherits one of each type of this allele, the coat is not dark brown, or part black, part brown. It will be completely black. The 'black fur' allele always wins. It is said to be **dominant**. The 'brown fur' allele is said to be **recessive**. It is still there, and could be passed on to the next generation, but it is weaker than the 'black fur' one and its effect is masked.

We usually choose a letter of the alphabet to represent an allele. Where there are two forms of an allele, a capital letter is used for the dominant allele, and the small letter for the recessive one. In this case, the 'black fur' allele is represented by **B** and the 'brown fur' one by **b**.

You can use a special type of table called a Punnett square to work out what would happen if a pure black guinea pig (with alleles **BB**) mated with a pure brown one (**bb**). The sperm produced by the black male would all contain allele **B**. Ova from the brown female all contain allele **b**.

This guinea-pig must have two 'brown fur' alleles as it has a brown coat.

	Possible alleles in gametes (ova)	Possible alleles in gametes (sperm)	
		B	B
	b	Bb	Bb
	b	Bb	Bb

It is easy to forecast what the babies will look like. However many babies are born, all must have allele **Bb**, so they will show the dominant black colour.

However, each baby carries both 'black fur' (**B**) and 'brown fur' (**b**) alleles.

Can you forecast what might happen if guinea-pigs which each have this **Bb** combination mate?

	Possible alleles in gametes (ova)	Possible alleles in gametes (sperm)	
		B	b
	B	BB	Bb
	b	Bb	bb

Four different arrangements are possible. One (BB) will give a 'pure' black baby. Two (Bb) will give black babies, because the 'black fur' allele is dominant. Only one (bb) will give a brown baby.

The chances of a black baby are three times greater than for a brown one. Over a large population, about three-quarters of the babies will be black. However, the combination of alleles in the particular sperm and ovum that join together are random. You can illustrate this with another example.

Male or female?

In humans, the diploid number is 46 – our cells contain 23 pairs of chromosomes. For 22 of these pairs, the two chromosomes match each other in the number and positions of the alleles. The final pair are so different that they are given different labels, X and Y. This pair of chromosomes determine the sex of a human baby. Females have two X chromosomes (XX) and males have one X and one Y (XY). How does this affect the chances of having a boy or a girl when a human baby is conceived?

Of the four possible combinations (each equally likely), two would give a boy and two a girl. Over the whole population, numbers of boys and girls are roughly equal. Because the mixing of alleles is random, however, you probably know families with different numbers of boys or girls. No matter how many male or female children are in a family, there is always an equal chance of any new baby being either male or female.

Mother (possible alleles in gametes – ova)	Father (possible alleles in gametes – sperm)	
	X	Y
X	XX	XY
X	XX	XY

Note that, since all human babies must inherit an X chromosome from their mother, the sex of a baby is determined by which allele is carried by the sperm that fertilises the egg.

The particular arrangement of alleles in an individual is called the **genotype**. The characteristics that develop as a result of these alleles make up the **phenotype** of the individual.

Things to do

1   Look back at the example of the 'tongue-rolling' gene. The two possible alleles are represented by T (dominant) and t (recessive). Draw Punnet square diagrams and use them to forecast the proportion of children who will be able to roll their tongue if the genotypes of the parents are:

    a Mother (TT) father (tt)

    b Mother (Tt) father (Tt)

Human females have two X chromosomes in their cells. Males have one X and one Y. Unlike the other pairs of chromosomes, X and Y are different in the number of genes they carry. The Y chromosome is shorter. Many genes which are on the X chromosome are missing from the Y. This means that males have only one copy of each of these genes.

Colour blindness

One such gene is related to colour vision. The dominant allele gives normal vision, the allele for defective vision is recessive. Since a female has two X chromosomes, she would only suffer from colour-blindness if both alleles were of the recessive type. However, males have only one copy of this gene, and if this is the recessive form, they will suffer from colour-blindness. About 4% of males have some degree of colour-blindness, less than 1% of women suffer the same problem.

Characteristics like colour-blindness, which are affected by genes on the part of the X chromosome which is missing from the Y chromosome, are said to be sex-linked, because they will affect males differently from females.

Haemophilia

Haemophilia is a condition which became widely known during the nineteenth century, because the Russian royal family suffered from it. It is caused by a recessive, sex-linked allele which is associated with blood clotting. Sufferers from haemophilia may suffer serious internal bleeding if they bruise themselves. Cuts do not easily heal because the blood does not clot properly (the way blood clots was described in *Keeping healthy*, Y10).

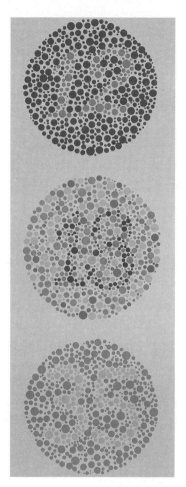

Opticians use circular pictures made up of coloured dots to test for restricted colour vision. Can you see the numbers in each chart?

Notice that a haemophiliac father cannot pass the condition on to his sons, but will pass the recessive allele on to his daughters. Because the allele is recessive, the daughter will not show any symptoms of haemophilia. However, the allele is present in all of her cells – she is a **carrier** for the condition. What will happen if a woman who is a carrier has children?

Healthy mother	Haemophiliac father	
	X_h	Y
XH	$X_H X_h$ (girl)	$X_H Y$ (boy)
XH	$X_H X_h$ (girl)	$X_H Y$ (boy)

The symbols XH and Xh are used for the two forms of the allele.

Half of the ova from the mother will carry the haemophilia allele.

There is a 50% chance that any sons of the family will suffer from haemophilia, and a 50% chance that any daughter will be a carrier.

By using charts like this to show the possible combinations of alleles, you can explain how it is possible to inherit haemophilia from your mother or grandfather, but not from your father!

Carrier mother	Healthy father	
	X_H	Y
X_H	$X_H X_H$	$X_H Y$
X_h	$X_H X_h$	$X_h Y$

Mixing genes is good for the species

Breeding is normally a random process. This is especially true of other plants and animals. Males and females meet by pure chance to produce offspring. Even though, in some human cultures, marriages are arranged by parents, it is much more usual for couples to just meet each other and fall in love.

Although some animals have specialised mating rituals that determine which is going to be successful in the mating game, it is usually just down to chance, which will mate with which.

There are very good reasons why breeding should be a chancy process. It ensures that all the genes in the population will be passed onto the next generation. This ensures that the gene pool is large and varied. We saw earlier in this unit that a large gene pool is essential to the survival of the species if the environment were to change.

The problem with random breeding is that you can never be sure just what characteristics the organism is going to have. This is true for humans, too. This is why some human cultures try to influence the choice of their children's marriage partner.

In the past, some political leaders have tried to influence our choice of partners on a massive scale. Adolf Hitler believed that the Aryan race should all be blue-eyed blondes and he took extreme measures to ensure that this happened.

Things to do

1 Draw Punnett square diagrams to show the possible outcomes for a baby born to a colour-blind father (Yc) and a mother who:

a has two of the dominant normal vision alleles (CC)

b is a carrier of the recessive colour-blindness allele (Cc).

7 Selective breeding

In natural selection, it is the external conditions in the environment which drive the process, and decide which plants or animals have the particular characteristics for breeding success. Selective breeding is done by making deliberate choices about which individual plants or animals will be parents. The principle is exactly the same as natural selection – those combinations of genes which produce the desired qualities will be selectively passed on.

Selective breeding has been used for thousands of years in agriculture to produce crops or animals with particular characteristics.

How to get a bigger egg

A flock of hens on a farm produce eggs of various different sizes. The reason for this is that egg size depends on many genes, not just one. Some hens have mostly genes for smaller eggs, some have more of the genes for larger eggs. The ova they produce will have different mixtures of genes and so produce eggs of different sizes.

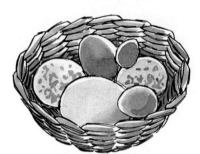

If a careful note is kept of the size of eggs from each hen, it is possible to choose just those hens who produce the largest eggs to be mated with a cockerel.

This careful record keeping can be repeated with the next generation of hens, then the next, and so on. At each generation, only those who produce the largest eggs are used for breeding.

Gradually, the genes for larger eggs become more widely spread in the flock, and the genes for smaller eggs become rarer. Eventually a limit is reached when all the eggs produced are large.

Also careful records can be kept of which cockerel produces chicks which give the largest eggs, so only certain cockerels are kept for breeding.

The records of the breeding history of an animal are called its pedigree. Pedigree records for many generations are kept for racehorses.

Why can't you get a really massive egg?

Selective breeding can only select those genes that are already there on the chromosomes. Once the farmer has managed to get a hen where all the genes that control egg size contain the 'large egg' alleles, then no matter how much more selective breeding the farmer does, the eggs will not get any bigger.

The gene pool of the hens has got smaller, because the farmer has not bothered to breed any hens that produce smaller eggs. All the genes for 'small egg size' have been lost.

Although the gene pool has been reduced, it has become much more stable. The farmer will have a flock of hens where all the genes for egg size are for 'large eggs'.

It will not matter which hen mates with which cockerel, as they will all produce large eggs.

Selective breeding can be used to select any desirable characteristic from any plant or animal.

Selective breeding – good or bad?

Selective breeding can develop characteristics which are valuable, but it reduces the variety in the gene pool for the species concerned. As a result of selective breeding, just 20 different high yielding cereal species produce most of the world's food. Join with a group to discuss the statements below, then use the information to make a poster either in favour or against using these carefully bred species on a farm.

Genetically pure crops are very reliable. They always grow in the same way.

High yield plants give more food from the land.

Plants can be bred to be farmed by machines. Cutting down the trees and hedges will let the machines work more efficiently and give bigger yields.

Some plants need very careful watering. If the weather is bad, the whole crop might fail

Modern varieties of plants have been bred to resist known crop diseases.

If a species with very little genetic variation is infected by a disease, the whole crop is likely to be affected, not just a few plants.

The seeds for specially bred crops may only be available from a few large suppliers. Supplies could be cut or stopped for commercial or political reasons or in case of war.

Because the seeds are produced by very large companies we don't have to rely on ourselves or local sources.

Things to do

1   Explain why farmers keep careful records of how much milk comes from each dairy cow.

2   All domestic dogs belong to the same species, but there are many different breeds, produced by selective breeding to give particular qualities. Find pictures and other information about some breeds of dog, and list the special features of each breed.

It has been known since the beginning of the 20th century that each gene, or section of a chromosome, carries instructions for the way in which an individual develops.

The processes that decide whether your eyes will be blue or brown, or whether your blood will clot properly are chemical processes The instructions stored in the genes must be able to cause the right chemical reactions in cells. How is this chemical code stored in each gene? Scientists only began to understand the answer in the 1960s when they were able to determine the chemical structure of chromosomes.

Hidden codes

All information has to be coded in some way.

You are reading this page because you understand the code for 'English'. It is quite a complicated code where 26 different letters are put together in different combinations to make words. The words are then put together in different combinations using a set of rules called grammar to make sentences. When you think of it this way, it is a wonder that any of us ever learn to read and write.

Fortunately the code for life is much simpler.

Chromosomes are made of a chemical called **DNA** (deoxyribose nucleic acid – deoxyribose is a type of sugar. You don't have to remember the name, only the initials!). This chemical consists of long chains of alternate sugar and acid molecules. Each sugar unit is also attached to a chemical called a **base**, which sticks out sideways from the chain.

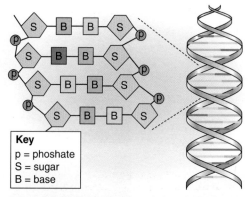

Key
p = phoshate
S = sugar
B = base

A strand of DNA showing the relationship between the sugars, acids and bases.

It is the arrangement of these bases which provides the code – and there are only four of them! You may not think that just four bases can make much of a code, but just try it for yourself.

Use the four letters A, C, G and T (they are the initial letters of the names of the four bases). Each piece of information in the genetic code is made up of a set of three bases. See how many different sequences of three you can make, taking any three of the four letters (the order matters, ACG is a different instruction to GCA and a set of three can include the same letter twice or three times).

You should find that you can make over 60 different instructions. By putting these instructions together into different sequences, cells can make all the chemicals necessary for life.

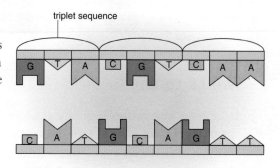

A strand of DNA showing detail of the bases. Each piece of information is made up of three bases – a triplet sequence.

Copying the code EV11

The DNA in a chromosome contains two strands wound together to form a double helix (rather like a spiral staircase).

The bases can only fit together in certain pairs (A with T, C with G).

Just before a cell divides, the DNA double spiral unwinds and the two strands separate.

The 'building bricks' of DNA (sugars, bases and acid) are always present in the cytoplasm of each cell.

As each section of a strand is exposed, new units can move in and fit against it, recreating the original partner strand. By the end of this process, the cell has two copies of the DNA, ready for cell division. Because the bases can only fit in certain combinations, each of the new chromosomes will be an exact copy of the original.

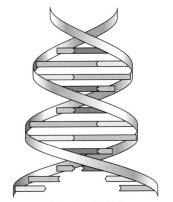

The double helix.
The lower end is beginning to separate.

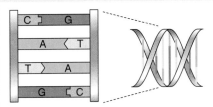

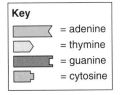

If you could straighten the spiral out, it would look rather like a ladder, with the sugar and acid chains as the side rails and the bases (A, C, G and T) as the rungs.

Key	
◄	= adenine
▷	= thymine
C	= guanine
▭	= cytosine

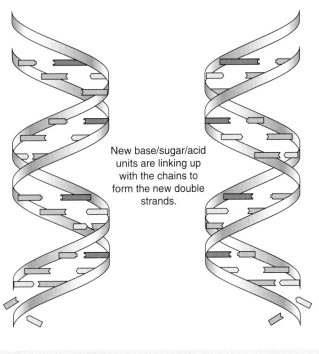

New base/sugar/acid units are linking up with the chains to form the new double strands.

DNA replicates itself during cell division.

❓ Things to do

1   Write a short note to a friend. Use a code where each letter is replaced by its position number in the alphabet. Tell your friend what the code is and see if they can decode the letter.

Putting the code to work EV12

Inside a living cell, copies are made of the sequence of bases which make up a gene. This copy (made of a chemical called RNA – ribonucleic acid – which is very like a single strand of DNA) passes into the cytoplasm of the cell. The immediate action of RNA is to link together amino acids to form a particular protein. In *Staying alive* (Y10), you learned about the reverse process in which digestion splits proteins down into separate amino acids.

The bases along the RNA strand work in groups of three. Each group matches a particular amino acid. The acids are assembled one at a time along the strand so that they can be linked in the correct order.

Only about 20 different amino acids are used in building proteins, and you have already seen that there are more possible sets of three which can be made from four different bases. Some sequences can be used as 'start' or 'stop' signals for protein building.

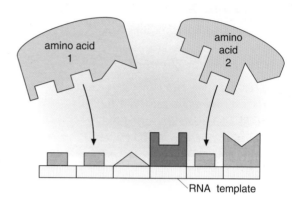

RNA template

What if things go wrong?

If something goes wrong during this protein building process, only the one cell will be affected. However, sometimes, things can go wrong inside the DNA, or when DNA is copied for cell division. The resulting cells will have the wrong blueprint for their chemical activity.

Changes in DNA are called mutations. They can be thought of as chemical 'mistakes'. Sometimes a base is missed out from the sequence, or an extra base gets put in, or the wrong base may be used. All of these events change the message of the affected gene, just as typing the wrong letter can muddle up a written message.

If the mutation takes place in an ovum or sperm cell, it will alter the development of the whole organism.

'The cat sat on the mutt.'

How do mistakes happen?

If a cell is exposed to ionising radiation, the energy carried by the radiation is enough to cause chemical changes. All living things are constantly exposed to natural radiation, as you saw in *Seeing inside the body* (Y11). This background radiation does occasionally cause mutations, and this is one of the sources of variation which make evolution possible.

Some chemicals can interfere with the process of cell division. They are said to be **mutagenic** (mutation causing). One possible effect of mutation is that cells run 'out of control', reproducing too quickly to form tumours. Chemicals which can increase the risk of cancer are called **carcinogens** and care is needed to avoid unnecessary contact with them.

The radiation hazard symbol.

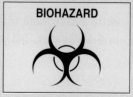

The biohazard symbol.

Spreading new genes quickly

Identifying a desirable gene, or engineering a new gene into an animal produces just one individual. Plant species can be cloned easily by taking small cuttings and growing them. It is not so easy to grow just part of an animal!

The most famous success with animals is probably the birth of a sheep called Dolly.

An ovum (egg cell) was taken from an ovary of Dolly's mother (sheep 1 in the diagrams). The nucleus was removed.

A body cell was taken from another sheep (sheep 2). The DNA from this cell was injected into the ovum. The ovum now contained a full diploid set of chromosomes, just as though it had been fertilised. All of this genetic material came from sheep 2.

The ovum was inserted into Dolly's mother's womb. The cell became implanted in the wall of the womb and grew. All of Dolly's body cells had exactly the same set of genes as sheep 2. Dolly was a clone!

This technique would make it possible to take many body cells from a sheep (or other animal) with desirable genes, and transfer the DNA into ova from many different surrogate mothers, so that many offspring could be produced to spread the genes quickly.

At present, there is still only a small chance that cells created in this way will implant successfully in the surrogate mother, so many attempts are needed to achieve success. Also, if chromosomes are taken from a mature donor, they are already 'old'. The cloned individual ages faster than normal and may be more susceptible to genetic illnesses.

The techniques are still being developed, and this is an area of science research that is likely to raise issues about how it is controlled or used for many years to come.

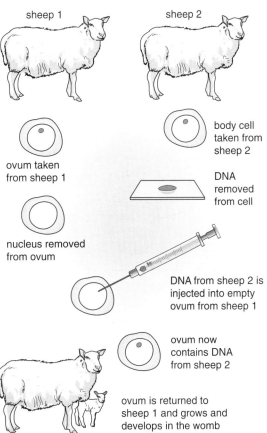

Scientists are perfecting techniques to clone whole organisms. Dolly the sheep was one example.

One possible use for these techniques would be to help preserve species like the giant panda, which are endangered in the wild and do not usually breed in captivity.

10 Genetic engineering

The newly-developing science of genetic engineering depends on two special features of the genetic code. Firstly, there is only one genetic code and it is the same in all species. Secondly, in a cell, the information from each gene can be read separately. The related section of the DNA double helix is opened up, so that the section of code can be copied and carried out into the cytoplasm.

This means that it is possible to take a gene from one species and **splice** it into DNA of another species. The gene will continue to produce its effect in the new species.

Some advantages (SS) EV13

- Diabetics used to inject themselves with insulin extracted from pigs and horses. This was a very expensive process and some diabetics were allergic to the drugs. Human insulin is now available. It is made by inserting the human insulin gene into bacteria which make the insulin. This can be extracted for use in humans.

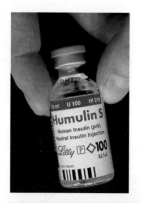

- Many people in Asia become blind through a lack of vitamin A in their diet of rice. Scientists have produced a variety of rice with a vitamin A gene inserted into its DNA. The genetically modified rice now makes vitamin A so people who eat it are less likely to suffer blindness due to vitamin deficiency.

- Food has been made to taste better and stay fresher for longer.

Some disadvantages

Genetically modified materials are becoming more common.

- No one really knows yet the long-term consequences of genetic engineering.
- Some people think that dangerous forms of new super bacteria may appear causing diseases we cannot treat.
- Some people think it is just wrong and that we should not interfere with 'nature'.

Things to do

1   You can use the Internet to find more information about genetic engineering. Use this information to produce lists of arguments for or against genetic engineering.

Genetic engineering – how it is done (SS) EV14

To produce rice which can make vitamin A, it was first necessary to identify the gene in carrots which carries the code for making vitamin A. The chromosome which carries this gene is treated with special enzymes called **restriction enzymes**. These cut out the required section of code (the 'vitamin A gene').

A chromosome from a rice plant is then cut open, and the vitamin A gene is linked into it, using enzymes called **ligases**. The changed chromosome can now be put back into a rice cell nucleus. When the cell is grown into a rice plant, the gene will be active and produce vitamin A. This rice plant can then be cloned to produce a breeding stock with the vitamin A gene.

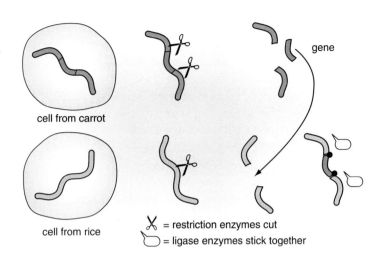

cell from carrot

cell from rice

gene

✂ = restriction enzymes cut
⬭ = ligase enzymes stick together

Genes from one organism can be removed and inserted into the genetic material of another organism. The characteristic will become part of the new organism.

Genes can be transferred to bacteria, too

Bacteria contain small loops of DNA called **plasmids**. These are easier to extract and alter than whole chromosomes.

The gene for making human insulin can be cut out from human DNA and inserted into a bacterial plasmid, which is then returned to the bacterium.

When a bacterium divides, it makes a copy of the plasmid so that each new bacterium receives a copy.

If the resulting bacteria are cultured. large numbers of clones (genetically identical cells) are produced, all of which make the human insulin protein. Insulin can be extracted and purified for use.

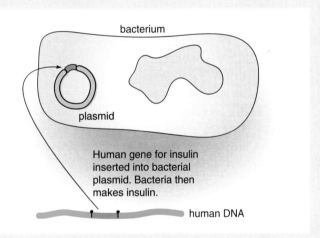

bacterium

plasmid

Human gene for insulin inserted into bacterial plasmid. Bacteria then makes insulin.

human DNA

The human gene for making insulin can be inserted into the bacterial plasmid. The bacteria will then make human insulin.

? Things to do

2 Look back at your work on diabetes in the unit *Keeping healthy* (Y10). Explain why sufferers from this condition may need to take insulin.

3 Molecules of pig or horse insulin are a slightly different shape to those of human insulin.

   a Explain why the shape of an enzyme is very important.

   b Suggest how this may cause some of the side effects of using insulin from other species.

1. Before about the year 1800, most peppered moths were light brown. They matched the colour of the tree bark they rested on. Occasionally, much darker peppered moths were seen. During the 19th century, soot from coal burning darkened tree trunks. Dark peppered moths became common, pale ones became rare. In the past 50 years, cleaner air has meant tree bark remains its natural colour.

   Use ideas about genetic variation to explain the change in the 19th century, and to predict how relative numbers of dark and light peppered moths have changed over the past 50 years.

2. Jean Baptiste de Lamarck proposed a theory of evolution long before Darwin. Find out the main differences between their theories and why Darwin's theory was accepted in place of Lamarck's.

3. Make two counters. Mark one with **X** on both sides, to represent the possible chromosomes from a mother. On the other counter, mark **X** on one side and **Y** on the other, to represent chromosomes from a father. Toss both counters and record whether they show **XX** or **XY**.

   Repeat as many times as possible. How many boys (**XY**) and how many girls (**XX**) do you get?

4. The gene for red hair is recessive.

   Mr and Mrs Black each have dark hair. Explain to them how their daughter can have red hair.

5. If a colour-blind man marries a normal-sighted woman with no history of colour-blindness in her family, what is the risk of:

   a any of their sons being colour-blind?

   b any of their daughters being colour-blind?

6. Red and white coat colour alleles are co-dominant in shorthorn cattle. Calves with one of each allele have mottled roan coats. What is the chance of a calf from a roan cow and a roan bull being:

   a red?

   b roan?

   c white?

7. A recent Salters GCSE examination question asked 'What is meant by an inherited characteristic?' One student answered 'It is something passed on from your parents, like your father's watch'. Explain why this answer is only partly right.

INTRODUCING
Sports science

Try these first

1 Energy is usually measured in:

  A m   B J   C N

2 Energy for muscles comes from respiration. This type of energy is called:

  A potential energy

  B kinetic energy

  C heat energy

  D chemical energy.

3 Cells obtain their energy by combining glucose with:

  A carbon dioxide   B oxygen   C nitrogen

4 Blood is pumped around the body by the:

  A arteries   B veins   C heart.

5 Air breathed out of lungs contains *less* of which chemical, compared with fresh air?

  A nitrogen   B oxygen   C carbon dioxide

The Fosbury flop is used by high jumpers. It gives better results than the straddle jump. Can you think of a scientific explanation for this?

In this unit you will learn:

- that energy transferred = work done
- work done (J) = force (N) × distance moved (m)
- power (W) = work done (J) ÷ time taken (s)
- how to measure your power and fitness
- about aerobic respiration in muscles
- how your body deals with aerobic respiration
- how blood transports energy to mucles
- about the different blood vessels in your body
- how your lungs get oxygen into your blood
- about the structure of the heart
- how muscles and bones move you around
- about the law of moments
- how to calculate kinetic and gravitational energy
- about energy conservation.

Work, power, fitness and technique are all important in breaking records in sport.

1 Sporting success

The training of a successful athlete involves much more than selecting a person with the right set of genes. Using the science of sport often decides the winner.

Marathon management

Jane decides to take part in a marathon. A marathon is a race over a distance of just over 42 kilometres, and needs a lot of careful preparation. The first stage in her preparation is for Jane to do a lot of running in the weeks and months leading up to the race. This improves her **fitness** by:

- building up her leg muscles
- training her heart muscle
- improving the operation of her lungs.

Jane can also prepare in the days before the race by eating a suitable diet. This provides her with the **energy** she will need to run the race.

Preparation is essential if a race is to be taken seriously.

Respiration

Jane will rely on her muscles to make this energy available during the race. The process by which our muscles transfer energy completes the cycle that begins when plants trap sunlight to drive photosynthesis and make foods. The overall effect of the oxidation of glucose in cells is like the reverse of photosynthesis, and it makes energy available to muscle cells.

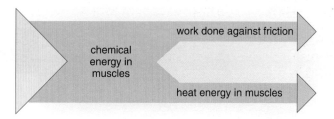

Energy transfer diagram for a marathon runner.

Some of the energy absorbed by Jane before the race is transferred by her muscles so that she can do **work** against air resistance and other sources of friction. The rest is transferred as heat energy in the cells of her muscles. Although this is not very useful, it cannot be avoided. No machine can ever transfer *all* of its energy into useful work.

Energy and work

All living things rely on energy to drive body processes such as:

- controlling body temperature
- growth
- movement
- repair of damaged tissue
- reproduction.

It is usually possible to measure the amount of energy transformed during any process, but not to measure the absolute total amount of energy in a system. We keep track of energy transfers using the concept of work.

work done = amount of energy transferred

What is work? SS1

You probably think that you are doing work while you read this. Easy or hard, it should still be work. What else are you at school for? The word 'work' has a special meaning in science.

Work is done whenever energy is transferred. In *Electricity in the home* (Y10), you learnt how to calculate the amount of electrical energy transferred in a circuit, and hence the amount of electrical work done. In this unit, you will study the mechanical work done when forces cause or alter movement – something you first studied in *Moving on* (Y10).

When the movement of an object is changed, its kinetic energy (the energy associated with its movement) changes. This change in energy is measured as the work done.

If a force causes an object to move, the amount of work done is calculated with this formula:

work = force × distance moved

If the distance is in metres (m) and the force in newtons (N), then the work is in joules (J).

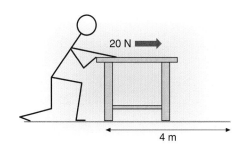

Sam pushes a table across the floor.

Energy conservation

An important idea in science is that energy cannot be created out of nothing, nor destroyed. It can only be 'changed' from one form to another. This is known as the **principle of conservation of energy**. How does this work in practice?

Sam pushes a table across the floor. He has to push it with a force of 20 Newtons. The table moves 4 metres. How much work does Sam do?

work = force × distance moved
= 20 × 4 = 80 J

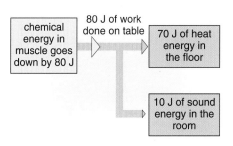

A flow chart showing the transfer of energy as Sam pushes the table.

So Sam transfers 80 joules of chemical energy in his muscles to the table. When Sam stops pushing, the table stops. Where has the energy gone now? As the table moves along, grinding against the floor, friction transfers that 80 joules to heat energy and a little sound energy.

? Things to do

1   The motto of the Olympic Games is *Citius, altius, fortius*. *Citius* means 'faster', and *altius* means 'higher'.

   a   List three sports where it is important to be able to go faster.

   b   List three sports where it is important to go higher.

   c   Find out what *fortius* means, and list three sports where it is important.

2   Joe lifts a 150 N weight through a distance of 2 m. How much work does he do?

3   Here are some situations:

   • holding a weight still above your head

   • stretching a rubber band

   • thinking out the answers to these questions.

   Which one involves doing some work?

2 Personal power

You know that many sports involve doing physical work. The people in these photographs are making their muscles work hard.

How would you describe the sprinters and oarsmen? You would probably use words like strong, fast and powerful. Each of these words has a special meaning in science, so you should use them carefully. In particular, power is often confused with strength and speed. **Power** is actually the rate at which something does work. It is calculated with this formula:

$$\text{power} = \frac{\text{work done}}{\text{time taken}}$$

If the work is in joules (J) and the time is in seconds (s), then the power is in watts (W).

Rowing, running, jumping, and throwing are all activities that require your muscles to do some work.

How much, how quickly? $\left(\text{SS}\right)$ SS2

Power depends on both how much work is done, and how quickly.

Joe and Bert work on a building site. Their job is to pull a rope hoist to lift bricks to the top of a 15 metres high building. Each brick weighs 10 newtons. Joe can lift 48 bricks and takes 60 seconds to lift them. Bert can only lift 40 bricks, but pulls them to the top in 48 seconds. Which of them is exerting the greater power?

Joe: 48 bricks lifted 15 m in 60 seconds

work done = force × distance moved
$\qquad$ = (48 × 10) × 15 = 7200 J

$$\text{power} = \frac{\text{work done}}{\text{time taken}}$$

$$= \frac{7200}{60} = 120 \text{ W}$$

Bert: 40 bricks lifted 15 m in 48 seconds

work done = force × distance moved
$\qquad$ = (40 × 10) × 15 = 6000 J

$$\text{power} = \frac{\text{work done}}{\text{time taken}}$$

$$= \frac{6000}{48} = 125 \text{ W}$$

In this example, although Joe is stronger, Bert exerts the greater power!

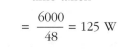

Joe and Bert each use a rope hoist to lift bricks. How can you tell who is the most powerful?

?

Things to do

1   Athletes can be **fast, powerful** and **strong.** Explain the scientific meaning of each of these words.

2   An electric kettle transfers 180 000 J of heat energy to water in 60 s. What is the power of the kettle?

3   Sam's maximum power is 120 W. How much work can he do in ten minutes?

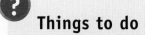

Finding out about fitness

There are two aspects of **fitness**. One is the ability to perform certain physical tasks. The second is the speed with which you recover after an activity.

Testing your muscle power

Some fitness tests begin by measuring the power of different muscles. Here is a way of doing this for your leg muscles.

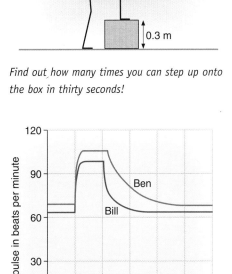

mass 40 kg

0.3 m

Find out how many times you can step up onto the box in thirty seconds!

Results

weight = 40 kg × 10 N/kg = 400 N
height of bench = 0.30 m
50 step-ups in 30 s

Calculation

$$\text{work done each step-up} = \text{force} \times \text{distance}$$
$$= 400 \times 0.30$$
$$= 120 \text{ J}$$

work done in 30 s = 120 × 50 = 6000 J

$$\text{power} = \frac{\text{work done}}{\text{time taken}}$$

$$= \frac{6000}{30} = 200 \text{ W}$$

If you do this, remember to use your own mass in the calculation (40 kg is just an example!)

Recovering after exercise

Hard physical activity can cause several changes to your body:

- you breathe more quickly and deeply
- your heart beats faster
- you sweat
- your muscles ache.

Graph of time taken for the pulse to return to normal after physical work.

If you are unfit it takes a long time for your body to return to normal. Fit people have short **recovery times**. The easiest way to measure recovery time is to see how long it takes for your heart beat (**pulse**) to return to normal.

The graph shows the pulse of two athletes before, during and after five minutes of hard physical work. Bill is fitter because his pulse returned to normal in the shortest time.

Things to do

4   Design an investigation to estimate the power of your arm muscles.

5   List the changes in your body when you do hard physical work.

6   Julie has a mass of 50 kg. She can climb up a flight of 40 stairs in a time of 20 s. Each step is 15 cm high. Gravity is 10 N/kg. How much power does she develop?

3 The muscle machine

Try this. Raise both of your hands above your head. You have just done some work, transferring chemical energy in your food to gravitational energy and heat energy.

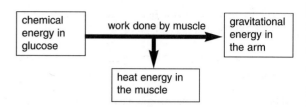

Energy transfers caused when muscles lift an arm.

A contracting muscle does work. It provides a moving force, so it transfers energy.

Muscles in the top half of your arms contract when you raise your arm. First the **biceps**, then the **triceps**. To lower the arm, both muscles relax and gravity pulls the arm down again.

Aerobic respiration

Glucose is the fuel which allows muscles to contract and do work. Glucose and oxygen are delivered to each muscle cell by the blood. These chemicals **diffuse** into the muscle cell through the cell membrane and are combined by the **mitochondria** with the help of enzymes.

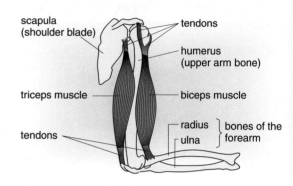

The arrangement of muscles in the human upper arm.

glucose + oxygen → carbon dioxide + water + energy

$$C_6H_{12}O_6 + 6O_2 \rightarrow 6CO_2 + 6H_2O + 2880 \text{ kJ}$$

The waste products of the reaction are carbon dioxide and water. They diffuse through the cell membrane into the blood and are carried away to the lungs where they are exhaled. This process where the cell produces energy in the presence of oxygen is called **aerobic respiration**.

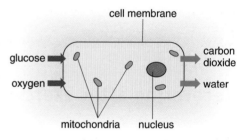

A cell showing the chemicals that diffuse across the cell membrane during work (cellular respiration).

? Things to do

1   This question is about aerobic respiration in a cell.

   a   Where does it happen?

   b   Write word and symbol equations for it.

   c   Name the reactants and products.

   d   How do the products enter and leave the cell?

2   Describe the energy transfers which take place when a muscle cell contracts.

3   Name the muscle that transfers energy when you lift your hand to your shoulder. Explain your answer.

The oxygen race

When athletes perform, they need lots of energy. Sometimes they cannot get all the energy they need from aerobic respiration:

- they cannot breathe fast enough to keep the oxygen level in the blood at the required level
- they cannot pump blood quickly enough to deliver the oxygen to the muscle cells.

When a muscle is working hard, it can easily use up oxygen faster than it can be delivered by the blood. The amount of dissolved oxygen in blood and tissues falls. The drop in blood oxygen levels triggers a number of changes:

- you breathe faster and deeper, increasing the rate at which oxygen enters the blood from the lungs
- the heart beats faster, speeding up the flow of blood from lungs to muscle.

Pulse and breathing rates do not return to normal until the **oxygen debt** has been repaid, and dissolved oxygen levels return to normal.

All athletes require time to repay the oxygen debt after a demanding race.

Anaerobic respiration SS4

Your body has a backup system called **anaerobic respiration**. The name means producing energy in the absence of oxygen. The cell obtains energy by converting glucose into **lactic acid**. This happens in the cytoplasm; the mitochondria are not involved. Only a small amount of energy is released.

glucose $\rightarrow$ lactic acid + energy

$$C_6H_{12}O_6 \rightarrow 2C_3H_6O_3 + 150 \text{ kJ}$$

This is far less energy efficient than aerobic respiration. The lactic acid is also poisonous. However, it does enable your muscles to carry on working for a little while when they cannot get enough oxygen.

Lactic acid in muscle cells causes pain, so you are discouraged from continuing anaerobic respiration for long. When the exercise stops, some of the lactic acid is oxidised away, and the remainder diffuses out from the muscle cells and the blood carries it to the liver, where it is converted to glycogen.

Things to do

4 Describe anaerobic respiration.

5 When do cells respire anaerobically?

6 Why is anaerobic respiration dangerous?

7 Describe and explain how the body deals with the waste products of anaerobic respiration.

8 Write a balanced symbol equation for the oxidation of lactic acid.

4 Energy transport in the body

Blood – the body's transport system SS5, SS6

Your circulatory system allows blood to transport food, hormones and oxygen to all parts of your body, and remove waste products, as follows:

- in the **lungs** blood picks up oxygen and loses carbon dioxide
- in the **liver** blood picks up glucose
- the **muscles** replace glucose and oxygen with water, carbon dioxide and heat energy
- the **skin** allows heat energy to escape
- the **kidneys** filter the blood to remove impurities and also control water loss from the body
- the **heart** increases the pressure, so that the blood can keep on flowing

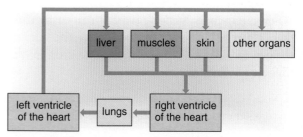

Flow chart to show the relationship between organs in the circulatory system.

Red blood cells

Blood contains millions of tiny cells called red blood cells. These cells are filled with a protein called **haemoglobin**. To make room for as much haemoglobin as possible, they have no nucleus.

In the lungs, oxygen diffuses into red blood cells and combines with haemoglobin to form bright red **oxyhaemoglobin**. Red blood cells are shaped like thin, flat discs to provide as much surface area as possible for oxygen to pass in or out.

As the oxygen is carried round the body, it diffuses out into muscles and other tissues. Blood which has little dissolved oxygen is a much darker, bluer colour.

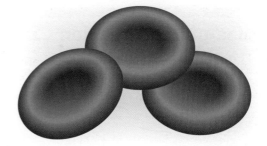

The disc-shape of the red blood cells gives them a large surface area for the exchange of oxygen with plasma.

Where does the blood go?

Blood circulates around the body in three different types of **blood vessel**. It leaves the heart in **arteries**, spreads through organs in **capillaries** and returns back to the heart in **veins**.

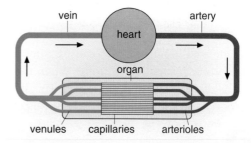

Three different types of blood vessel form the circulatory system.

Arteries

Arteries carry blood away from the heart and around the body. The walls are thick with muscle and elastic tissue to withstand the high pressure of the blood flowing through them. The hole inside them (the **lumen**) is therefore relatively small.

Arteries gradually divide and become smaller. The small arteries (called **arterioles**) connect to the capillaries.

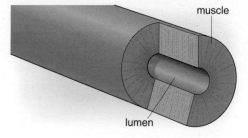

This cutaway section of an artery shows the thick, muscular walls and small lumen.

Capillaries

Capillaries have thin walls. The blood in them moves relatively slowly and has a lower pressure than in arteries.

The thin walls prevent blood cells and large proteins from leaving the capillary, but a large proportion of the plasma seeps out through the walls to bathe the surrounding cells.

This **tissue fluid** contains the dissolved glucose and oxygen which the cells need to respire. Carbon dioxide and other waste from the cells can diffuse into the tissue fluid. This is collected up into the capillaries and carried away in the blood.

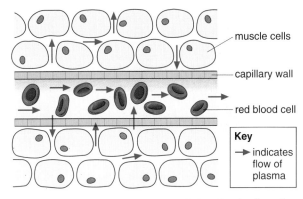

Plasma can pass through capillary walls but blood cells and large molecules remain inside the capillaries.

Veins

Capillaries join together to form slightly larger vessels called **venules**. Venules merge to produce **veins** which transport blood back to the heart.

The blood in veins is at a much lower pressure than in capillaries, so veins do not need thick walls. This means that they have a much wider lumen than arteries. Veins have flaps inside them. These act as valves to prevent the blood flowing in the wrong direction.

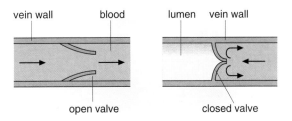

Valves in veins prevent blood flowing backwards.

? Things to do

1 Check back over the work you did in *Keeping healthy* (Y10). Write notes about what each component of the blood does:

   a plasma

   b red blood cells

   c white blood cells

   d platelets.

2 Blood passes through five different types of blood vessels between leaving the heart and entering it again. Name them in the correct order.

3 Describe and explain the structure of arteries.

4 Explain how substances in capillary blood reach the surrounding cells.

5 Describe and explain the structure of veins.

Getting oxygen into the body (SS) SS7

Every process in your body needs the supply of energy that is made available through respiration.

The glucose for this comes from the food you eat. It is carried round the body dissolved in the blood plasma. Reserve supplies are stored in the liver as glycogen (an insoluble polymer made by linking glucose molecules together).

The oxygen which is needed for respiration comes from the air.

Your lungs manage this process in the following way.

When you breathe in, air is drawn in through your mouth and passes down the **trachea**.

The air then passes through a **bronchus** into one of the lungs. Each bronchus splits into a large number of **bronchiole**s. At the end of each bronchiole is a dead end, an air sac. Bulges on the air sac form the **alveoli**.

Capillaries surround each alveolus, allowing the blood in them to get close to the air. In this way, although each alveolus is small, there are so many of them that there is enough surface area of air in contact with blood.

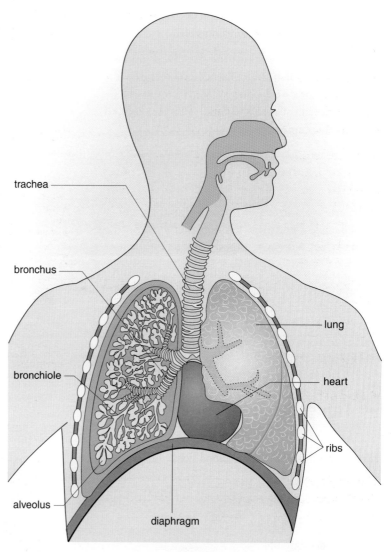

Section through the head and chest to show the heart, lungs, ribs and diaphragm.

? Things to do

1. What are the structures involved in breathing?
2. What are the two functions of the lungs?

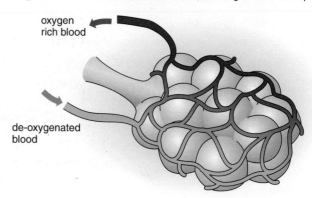

There is a rich blood supply to each alveolus.

Gas exchange in the alveolus

An alveolus is surrounded by capillaries. Oxygen and carbon dioxide diffuse between the blood and the air. Since diffusion is the random movement of molecules, it is a slow process. It is speeded up in an alveolus by having:

- a thin wall between the air and the blood
- a moist surface next to the air
- lots of capillaries around it.

Blood entering the lungs has a low concentration of oxygen, lower than the air in the alveolus. Oxygen diffuses into the blood in the surrounding capillaries.

At the same time, carbon dioxide diffuses from the blood into the air. To maintain this essential flow of molecules, the air in each alveolus must be regularly replaced with fresh air from outside the lungs. This is the process of **breathing** and it happens by making the lungs expand and contract regularly.

The lining of the bronchi and bronchioles is covered with hair-like projections called villi. The waving movement of the villi moves mucus and dust out of the lungs. Tobacco smoke can damage the action of the villi.

Breathing

Place your hands on your ribs. Breathe in and out a few times. Can you feel the movement of your ribs?

The lung volume can also be controlled by the **diaphragm**. This is a flat muscle at the base of the rib cage, above the stomach.

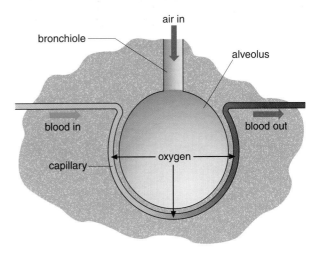

Oxygen diffuses through the moist wall of an alveolus into the blood in the surrounding capillaries.

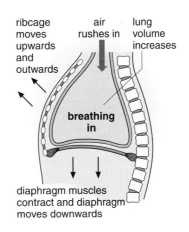

ribcage moves upwards and outwards — air rushes in — lung volume increases

breathing in

diaphragm muscles contract and diaphragm moves downwards

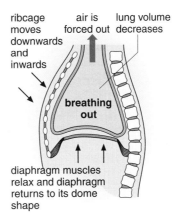

ribcage moves downwards and inwards — air is forced out — lung volume decreases

breathing out

diaphragm muscles relax and diaphragm returns to its dome shape

When the diaphragm contracts, the lungs expand, allowing them to fill with fresh air. Relaxing the diaphragm allows the lungs to contract, expelling stale air.

? Things to do

3   What is an air sac? How is it adapted to allow the flow of gases in and out of the blood?

4   Explain how the ribs and diaphragm replace stale air in an air sac with fresh air.

5   Suggest why smoking can make people more likely to suffer from lung diseases.

THE FERRERS SCHOOL

6 Pumping blood around the body

Your **heart** is the pump that forces your blood to circulate around your body. The muscles in your heart have been contracting and relaxing since before your birth, and will only stop with your death.

The human heart is really two pumps joined together! Blood returning from the body through veins enters the right side of the heart and is pumped to the lungs, where carbon dioxide can diffuse out, and fresh oxygen is absorbed.

The oxygen-rich blood from the lungs enters the left hand side of the heart, and is pumped out to all other parts of the body.

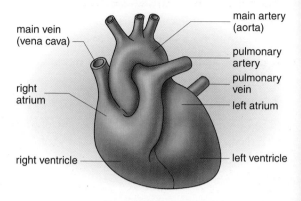

The human heart is about the size of an adult's clenched fist. You can see the main blood vessels.

The structure of the heart

Each side of the heart has two chambers:

- blood returning from veins enters the atrium (upper chamber)
- the atrium contracts
- blood is forced through a semi-lunar valve into the ventricle (lower chamber)
- the ventricle contracts, forcing blood out through the arteries.

The valves in the veins and between the atrium and ventricle are very important. They make the blood take the correct path out of a chamber when its muscle contracts.

The left ventricle has to pump blood all round the body, so it has a larger muscle than the right ventricle. Also, too large a pressure in the pulmonary artery damages the lungs.

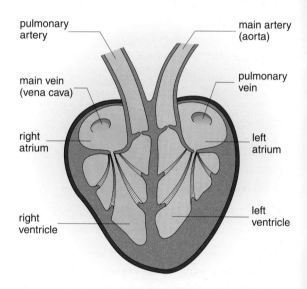

A section through the heart shows the way it is divided into four chambers.

Healthy hearts

The heart muscles are doing work all the time, so they need their own supply of glucose and oxygen. If the arteries delivering blood to the heart muscle become blocked, the heart can stop working properly. This can be avoided by eating a suitable diet. Like all muscles, the heart can be made stronger with exercise, so making the heart beat faster regularly makes you fitter.

? Things to do

1   Describe each stage as blood returning from the body passes through the heart and lungs and back out to the body.

Sports science

Developing theories about blood circulation

This page gives some information about two doctors who each helped to advance knowledge about blood circulation. Think how each of their theories helped to explain the evidence that was available to them at the time.

Galen's theory

Galen worked in Rome in about 200 AD. He was the first doctor to use the pulse as an aid to diagnosis. He believed that blood was made in the liver (using food absorbed from the gut), then pumped by the heart to the body, where it was used up. He also believed that blood moved with a backward and forward motion (which he thought explained the pulse), and that blood passed backwards and forwards between the ventricles through holes in the central wall (septum).

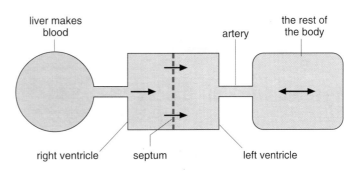

A scheme of the body's blood supply as viewed by Galen in about 200 AD.

Harvey's theory

William Harvey's theory was published in 1628. He explained the functions of the four chambers of the heart, the lungs, arteries and veins. He could not see capillaries, but assumed that tiny blood vessels must link the arteries and veins. This theory guided later workers with improved microscopes, who discovered capillaries and so completed the theory.

Different types of evidence

In ancient Rome, dissection of human bodies was forbidden by law. Galen worked from external evidence, and dissection of animals. Galen's theories were supported by the church, which effectively banned discussion of any alternative ideas. Harvey was allowed to dissect human bodies. He discovered the valves in veins and the heart. He was also able to measure the size of the heart. He multiplied this by the number of heart-beats and calculated that a human heart pumps about 5 tonnes of blood each day! This much blood could not be made every day, so he concluded that the blood must flow in a closed circulation. This in turn led him to suggest that capillaries must exist to complete the circuit between arteries and veins.

William Harvey was the first scientist to describe the circulation of blood.

? Things to do

2 What advantages were available to Harvey and later workers, but not to Galen?

3 Which discovery by Harvey showed that the blood did not flow backwards and forwards in the blood vessels?

4 In what way did Harvey's theory guide later workers to make further discoveries?

7 Muscles and bones

Muscles help you to move around. However, muscles can only exert forces by **contracting**. So muscles can't push, they can only pull. The bones that the muscles are connected to are also important for movement.

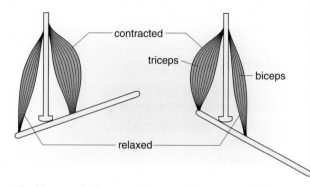
The biceps and triceps muscles move the arm up and down.

Muscles work in pairs SS8

The muscles which move you around have their ends anchored to bones by **tendons**. The diagram shows the pair of muscles in your upper arm which move your forearm up and down.

The forearm is tilted up and down by the **biceps** and **triceps** muscles. The top ends of both of these muscles are connected to the bones of the shoulder. The bottom ends are connected to the forearm bones, on different sides of the **elbow joint**. To raise the forearm the biceps contracts and the triceps relaxes. To lower the forearm, the biceps relaxes and the triceps contracts.

Levers SS9, SS10

The bones in your body are **levers** which are pulled around by muscles. For example, look how the biceps muscle turns the lower arm to lift loads. A lever does one of two jobs. It is either a **force multiplier** or a **distance multiplier**.

Force multipliers

The pivot is nearer to the **load** than to the **effort**. A small **effort force** (what you put in) will move a larger **load force** (the job you are trying to do). A crowbar is a simple example of this type of lever, with the pivot between the load and the effort.

A small force on the screwdriver causes a large force on the lid.

Sometimes the load force and effort force are on the same side of the pivot. A wheelbarrow is an example of this type of lever.

All force multipliers have the load force acting closer to the pivot than the effort force. By increasing the distance of the effort force from the pivot, the load force can be made larger.

Distance multipliers

Some levers turn a small movement by the effort force into a large movement for the load. A fishing rod works in this way – a small movement of the hand causes a large movement at the tip of the rod.

Fishing with a rod is an example of a lever that acts as a distance multiplier.

Bones as levers

Take another look at the effect that the biceps has on the forearm. Each time that the biceps contracts (and the triceps relaxes), the forearm is rotated about the elbow joint (the **pivot**). The biceps applies a **turning force, or moment,** to the forearm (the **lever**).

Moments

The turning effect of a force is called its moment. The moment is calculated using the formula:

moment = force × distance from pivot

So if the biceps applies an upwards force of 240 N, at a distance of 5 cm (0.05 m) from the elbow joint, the turning force can be calculated:

moment = 240 × 0.05 = 12 Nm

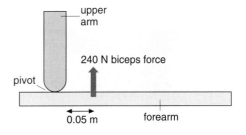

Moment = force × distance from pivot.

Balancing moments

A lever can turn around its pivot either clockwise or anti-clockwise. A single moment will make the lever turn. To balance a lever, moments in opposite directions are needed, that just balance each other out. This is known as the **law of moments**.

This law can be used to calculate the load at the end of the arm that can just be held up by this muscular effort.

clockwise moment = anticlockwise moment
$$F \times 0.3 = 12 \text{ Nm}$$
$$F = \frac{12}{0.3} = 40 \text{ Nm}$$

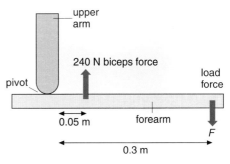

Clockwise moment = anticlockwise moment.

In the calculation above, it was assumed that the arm itself has no weight. Of course, this is not true, so the biceps has to hold up the arm, as well as the load in the hand!

The weight of the arm acts halfway along its length. So the moment due to the weight of the arm and the moment of the load together must just balance the moment of the biceps muscle.

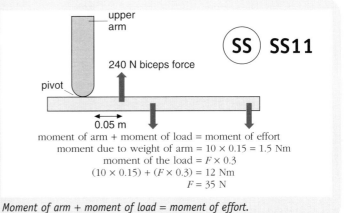

SS SS11

moment of arm + moment of load = moment of effort
moment due to weight of arm = 10 × 0.15 = 1.5 Nm
moment of the load = $F \times 0.3$
(10 × 0.15) + ($F \times 0.3$) = 12 Nm
$F = 35$ N

Moment of arm + moment of load = moment of effort.

Things to do

1 In the picture on the previous page, Joy pushes down on the end of the screwdriver with a force of 60 N. Her hand is 20 cm from the edge of the tin. The extra distance to the end of the screwdriver is 0.4 cm. What is the upward force on the lid of the tin?

8 Faster and higher

Going up (SS) SS12, SS13

When this high jumper springs upwards to try to clear the bar, he is using his muscles to do work. He wants to gain enough **gravitational potential energy** (PE) to get over the bar.

The force of gravity pulls everything down towards the Earth. To move up, work must be done against the force of gravity.

Imagine lifting an athlete of mass m kilograms through a vertical height of b metres. His weight will be mg newtons, where g = 10 newtons per kilogram, the strength of gravity at the surface of the Earth.

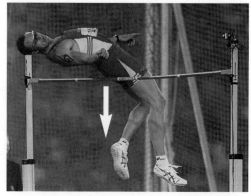

The downward arrow shows the weight (downward force) of the athlete.

Sprinting along

When this sprinter pushes off from the starting blocks, she is using her muscles to do the work. She wants to increase her **kinetic energy** (KE) as quickly as possible.

The kinetic energy of an object of mass m kilograms, moving at a speed of v metres per second is given by;

$$KE = \frac{1}{2} mv^2$$

Rolling downhill

Wherever an object is, it has some gravitational potential energy. If it rises higher, this energy increases, if it moves to a lower level, the potential energy decreases. However, the total energy must remain the same. As an object moves lower, the potential energy it loses is often transferred to movement – kinetic energy.

This water chute is very smooth and slippery. The top is 5 metres higher than the bottom. Anita, mass 30 kilograms, slides down. What speed has she reached by the time she gets to the bottom?

$$
\begin{aligned}
\text{PE (at top)} &= mgh \\
&= 30 \times 10 \times 5 \\
&= 1500 \text{ J} \\
\text{KE (at bottom)} &= \frac{1}{2} mv^2 \\
1500 &= \frac{1}{2} \times 30 \times v^2 \\
v^2 &= 100 \\
\text{so } v &= 10 \text{ m/s}
\end{aligned}
$$

Starting blocks help an athlete gain kinetic energy as quickly as possible.

All of the potential energy Anita had at the top of the slide turns to kinetic energy as she comes down.

Energy conservation SS14

The important thing about these calculations is that the shape of the chute and ramp doesn't matter – just the vertical height of the drop or rise. This makes the potential and kinetic energy equations very useful. This is because energy is **conserved**.

The amount of energy does not change when it is transferred.

If friction is very small, then any change of potential energy results in an equal change of kinetic energy. However, if friction is *not* small, then some of the energy will be transferred to heat energy. Energy will still be conserved, but you won't be able to use the energy equations so easily!

Non-useful energy SS15

Suppose that Anita arrives at the bottom of the water chute with a speed of only 8 metres per second. We can use this to calculate how much non-useful heat energy was transferred from her potential energy.

$E_p = 1500$ J
$E_k = \frac{1}{2} mv^2$

$= 0.5 \times 30 \times 8 \times 8 = 960$ J
energy transferred to heat $= 1500 - 960 = 540$ J

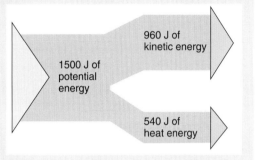

Energy transfers, allowing for friction, while sliding down a chute.

Working out the best design

Designers use calculations like these. In a 10-pin bowling alley, the balls, which have a mass of 3 kilograms, roll back to the player at 2 metres per second. At the end of the runway, they roll up a ramp so that they are at a convenient height for the player to pick them up. How high can this platform be?

KE of the ball $= \frac{1}{2} mv^2$

$= 0.5 \times 3 \times 2 \times 2 = 6$ J

The maximum height the ball can roll up to would be where all of this kinetic energy is converted to potential energy, that is 6 joules of energy:

PE of the ball $= mgh$

$= 3 \times 10 \times h$

$h = \frac{6}{30} = 0.2$ metres

A ramp at 20 cm high makes it easier for players to pick the balls up, and also stops them from crashing into the end of the runway!

So the ramp is designed to be 20 centimetres high.

? Things to do

1. Explain why high jumpers take a run-up, instead of jumping from the spot.

2. Tom is bouncing on a trampoline. His mass is 25 kg and he takes off from the trampoline at 3 m/s. How high above the trampoline will his feet be at the top of the bounce?

3. Bobby's mass is 72 kg and Anita's is 30 kg. They dive off a board which is 2 metres above the water.

   a. Calculate the speed at which Bobby lands in the water.

   b. Calculate the speed at which Anita lands in the water.

1 The average force used to stretch a rubber band by 10 cm is 5 N.

   a How much work is needed to stretch the band?

   b How much elastic energy does the band gain? Where did that energy come from?

2 Jo has a mass of 60 kg. She climbs a mountain, moving a vertical distance of 2 km. (g = 10 N/kg.)

   a How much work does she do?

   b She transfers 3.6 MJ of chemical energy in her muscles during the climb. How much of this is transferred to heat energy?

3 A car at full speed has a power of 15 kW.

   a How much work does the car do when going at full speed for a minute?

   b The top speed is 30 m/s. How far does the car go in a minute?

   c Use your answers to **a** and **b** to calculate the force of air resistance on the car.

4 Alice is training for a marathon race. Explain how she could use measurements of her pulse rate to track her improving fitness.

5 Respiration and breathing are not the same thing. Explain the meaning of each.

6 Aerobic respiration can happen in muscle cells.

   a Write out a word equation for aerobic respiration.

   b Explain how the reactants and products enter and leave the cell.

7 In a short race, muscles can respire anaerobically.

   a Explain why this may be necessary.

   b Why does anaerobic respiration hurt?

   c Explain how your body deals with the waste products of anaerobic respiration.

8 Describe the changes to blood as it passes through various organs in the body.

9 Describe how red blood cells transport gases between the air and muscle cells.

10 Write notes about the structural differences between arteries, veins and capillaries.

11 Describe how your lungs are adapted to provide efficient transfer of gases between blood and the air.

12 Read about Galen's theory of the heart (page 155).

   a Both Harvey and Galen wrote in Latin. What were the advantages and disadvantages of doing this?

   b Describe the experimental evidence that proves that Galen's theory is wrong.

   c Harvey had a lot of difficulty in getting his theory accepted. Was this a good thing?

13 Draw an example of a lever used as a force multiplier. Label the pivot, lever, effort and load.

14 Most of the muscles and bones in your body are arranged as distance multipliers.

   a Draw a diagram of an example.

   b Why are muscles arranged in pairs?

15 A lever is pivoted at its centre. A 50 N load is placed 0.2 m from the pivot. Calculate where a 200 N effort could be placed to balance the lever.

16 A 5 kg rock is dropped down a well which is 30 m deep. There is no friction.

   a How much potential energy does the rock lose?

   b How fast is the rock moving when it hits the water?

INTRODUCING

Burning and bonding

Try these first

A burning candle is covered with a beaker.

1   Which gas in the air is needed for the candle to burn?

2   Why does the candle go out?

A Bunsen burner can be adjusted to produce different flames.

3   How is the Bunsen burner adjusted to get a yellow or luminous flame?

4   How is the Bunsen burner adjusted to get a blue or non-luminous flame?

5   Which flame is hotter?

Burning is a chemical change. The materials which are burning in this building are combining with oxygen to form new substances.

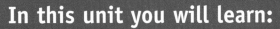

In this unit you will learn:

● burning is a reaction of a substance with oxygen releasing energy in the form of heat and light

● the total mass of the reactants is equal to the mass of the products

● complete combustion of a hydrocarbon produces carbon dioxide and water vapour

● incomplete combustion of hydrocarbons produces poisonous carbon monoxide and water vapour

● energy is needed to break bonds and is released when bonds are formed

● in an exothermic reaction more energy is released from forming new bonds than is used to break existing bonds

● there are two types of bonding in compounds – ionic and covalent

● patterns in properties of elements can be explained using the Periodic Table.

Why do you think this cyclist is wearing a mask?

An early idea about burning

Three hundred years ago scientists did not know what happened during burning. They thought that when substances burned they lost a substance called phlogiston.

They thought a piece of wood could burn easily because it contained a lot of phlogiston. Burning was thought to be a process by which the wood lost phlogiston. The phlogiston came out into the air (they could see, and sometimes smell, fumes coming out) and the ash which was left behind wouldn't burn any more because it had no phlogiston left. This was the first attempt at a theory to explain burning.

phlogiston

wood ⟶ burns ⟶ ash

Antoine Lavoisier was the scientist who produced experimental evidence that led to a new theory of burning as combustion. He had a chemical balance that could weigh accurately to 0.005 grams. He was able to detect small mass changes when substances burned.

First experiment

1 sunlight focused on surface of mercury

2 mercury combines with oxygen from air in the jar as it is heated by sunlight

3 water rises ($\frac{1}{5}$ way up) in bell jar as oxygen gas is used up in burning

4 a film of red powder (mercury oxide) is formed

Lavoisier burned some mercury in a flask of air. He found that:

● no more than one fifth of the air was used up.

● the air that remained would not support burning or living things.

Second experiment

5 red powder heated

retort

furnace

7 volume of trapped air increases (by $\frac{1}{5}$) as oxygen gas is given off

6 bubbles rise through water into trapped air in bell jar

The mercury was changed to a red solid that he called mercury calx. The mercury calx was heavier than the mercury it was made from.

When he heated some of this mercury calx (we now call it mercury oxide), he got back mercury and a gas in which things burned brightly. This was the gas oxygen. Lavoisier realised that in the burning process, mercury was combining with oxygen. He also realised that if all the reacting substances (mercury and oxygen) are taken into account, the total mass of material does not change during the chemical reaction.

New ideas about burning

A theory is useful while it helps to explain the evidence known at the time. If new evidence is found which does not fit with the theory, then the theory must be amended or even abandoned. Thus, the way we think about the world around us depends on the evidence we find. It is important to be able to design experiments in order to collect evidence that is reliable and accurate. You can gain credit for this skill in your coursework assessment.

We now know that burning involves a permanent chemical change. The burning materials combine with oxygen from the air to produce new substances.

The French scientist Antoine Lavoisier in his laboratory with the equipment he used in his experiments on burning.

During burning there are changes in the way atoms are bonded together. The atoms which were bonded together in the burning material become bonded to oxygen atoms. Forming these new bonds releases energy.

The Bunsen burner (SS) BB1

A Bunsen burner uses natural gas (or bottled gas) as the fuel to produce a flame that can be controlled to give different temperatures.

When the air hole is open a plentiful supply of air gets into the burner, and a mixture of gas and air burns completely to produce carbon dioxide and water vapour. This is called the non-luminous flame and has a high temperature. When the air hole is closed little air can enter, and the gas is not as completely burned. The yellow or luminous flame is much cooler and contains particles of soot. It does not, however, produce poisonous carbon monoxide, because plenty of air can get to the flame.

Air hole open in the Bunsen burner gives a non-luminous flame.

Air hole closed in the Bunsen burner gives a luminous flame.

When a fuel such as natural gas burns in a limited supply of air, such as a badly serviced gas fire, poisonous **carbon monoxide** may be produced. Up to 50 people each year in the United Kingdom die of the effects of carbon monoxide poisoning.

? Things to do

1 What facts about things that burn could be explained by the Phlogiston Theory?

2 A piece of magnesium weighs 0.24g. When it is burnt the ash weighs 0.40g.

   a Explain why this change of mass occurs.

   b Why is this change of mass difficult to explain using the Phlogiston Theory?

3 Describe the differences between the two types of Bunsen burner flame.

4 Neil rents a house out to students. He has to have a gas certificate each year from a qualified gas engineer.

   a Why is this?

   b The students try to block all the ventilation ducts into the house. Why could this be dangerous?

5 a Complete the following word equation for the complete combustion of methane.
      Methane + oxygen → _____ + _____

   b Finish and balance the symbol equation for the same reaction.
      CH_4 + O_2 → _____ + _____

2 Cars and air pollution

When a car has an MOT test the emissions from the engine exhaust have to be measured. If the levels of pollutants are too high the car fails its MOT test. Where do these pollutants come from?

What happens inside a car's engine?

The main part of the car engine consists of hollow cylinders – four in most cars. Each cylinder has an inlet valve through which a mixture of petrol vapour and air is drawn in.

It also has an outlet valve through which the waste gases are forced out. There is a spark plug in the cylinder that ignites the petrol–air mixture by an electronically produced spark. The exploding mixture pushes a piston down, which turns a shaft and makes the car move.

What happens during the explosion? Ideally all of the petrol burns with oxygen from the air to form carbon dioxide and water.

octane + oxygen → carbon dioxide + water

$$2\ C_8H_{18} + 25\ O_2 \rightarrow 16\ CO_2 + 18\ H_2O$$

① a inlet valve opens
b piston moves down
c petrol–air mixture drawn into cylinder

② a both valves closed
b piston moves up, compressing the petrol–air mixture

④ a exhaust valve opens
b piston moves up, pushing exhaust gases out of cylinder

③ a spark plug ignites petrol–air mixture
b expanding hot gases push down piston

The four-stroke cycle of an internal combustion engine.

But what happens in practice differs from the theory:

- The petrol is not all burned so the exhaust gases contain some unburned hydrocarbons. Hydrocarbons are greenhouse gases. Methane is 70 times more effective than carbon dioxide at stopping radiation leaving the Earth.
- Some of the carbon in the hydrocarbon is converted into carbon monoxide, rather than carbon dioxide.

octane + oxygen → carbon monoxide + water

$$2\ C_8H_{18} + 17\ O_2 \rightarrow 16\ CO + 18\ H_2O$$

Carbon monoxide is extremely poisonous. It is absorbed by haemoglobin in the blood and prevents the haemoglobin transporting oxygen around your body.

- Because the temperature in the engine is very high, some of the nitrogen in the air combines with some of the oxygen to form oxides of nitrogen, NO_x. These gases include nitrogen monoxide (NO) and nitrogen dioxide (NO_2). These gases contribute to acid rain.

 Things to do

1 Write a word and balanced symbol equation for the reaction taking place in the first chamber of a catalytic converter when nitrogen monoxide and carbon monoxide react.

2 Write word and symbol equations for the reaction taking place in the second chamber that removes unreacted octane, C_8H_{18}.

3 Why is extra air added between the first and second chambers?

Reducing the pollution from cars

One way of cutting down on the more powerful pollutants in exhaust gases is to use a catalytic convertor.

This is a pipe containing a honeycomb structure coated with tiny particles of platinum. The platinum acts as a catalyst, speeding up reactions which:

- reduce the oxides of nitrogen
- oxidize unburned hydrocarbons and carbon monoxide.

Catalytic converters have two chambers, because two separate stages of reaction are needed. In the first chamber, oxygen is taken from the oxides of nitrogen (leaving harmless nitrogen) and transferred to carbon monoxide, turning it into the less harmful carbon dioxide.

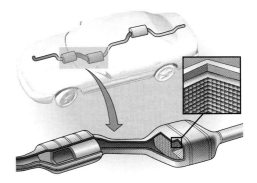

The two chambers of a catalytic converter can be fitted within the exhaust system of most cars.

The second stage needs oxygen from air, so some air is drawn into the pipe between the chambers. In the second chamber, oxygen from this air oxidises any unburned hydrocarbons to carbon dioxide and water. It also oxidises any remaining traces of carbon monoxide to carbon dioxide.

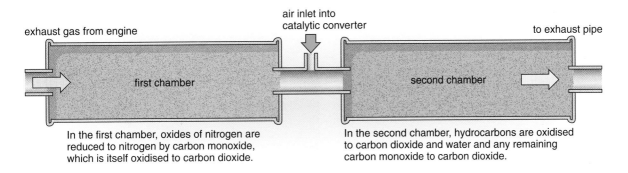

exhaust gas from engine | air inlet into catalytic converter | to exhaust pipe

first chamber | second chamber

In the first chamber, oxides of nitrogen are reduced to nitrogen by carbon monoxide, which is itself oxidised to carbon dioxide.

In the second chamber, hydrocarbons are oxidised to carbon dioxide and water and any remaining carbon monoxide to carbon dioxide.

? Things to do

4 Draw a box to represent a car engine. Add labelled arrows to show the substances that go into the car engine and the substances that come out.

5 Why are catalytic convertors expensive?

6 Suggest why catalytic convertors have a honeycombed structure.

7 Suggest why having the platinum in a powdered form is better than having it in a single lump.

8 Suggest a theory that would explain the action of the catalyst in a catalytic convertor. Explain why a catalytic convertor cannot be used on a car that burns leaded petrol.

9 In some cities the use of cars has to be controlled to prevent air pollution becoming too serious. One such city is Santiago in Chile. This is in a deep valley where pollutants can collect and remain. Every day only cars with certain digits at the end of the registration number are allowed to enter the city. Even so the problem is worsening. Suggest ways in which the atmospheric conditions in the city could be improved.

10 It has been suggested that large numbers of trees should be planted. Explain how this could reduce the effects of pollution from the motor car.

What happens when a hydrocarbon fuel burns?

SS BB2

The picture shows natural gas (methane) burning. This reaction can be summarised by the following word and symbol equations:

methane + oxygen $\longrightarrow$ carbon dioxide + water + energy

started by heating

$$CH_4 + 2\,O_2 \rightarrow CO_2 + 2\,H_2O + energy$$

(in the form of heat and light)

This shows that a molecule of:

- methane (CH_4) contains one carbon atom and four hydrogen atoms

- oxygen (O_2) contains two oxygen atoms

- carbon dioxide (CO_2) contains one carbon atom and two oxygen atoms

- water (H_2O) contains two hydrogen atoms and one oxygen atom

From the equation, for every methane molecule burned, two molecules of oxygen are used. One molecule of carbon dioxide and two molecules of water are formed. The forces holding atoms together within these molecules are called **chemical bonds**.

Natural gas, or methane, is the simplest hydrocarbon fuel. A flame shows energy being released in the form of light and you can feel the heat.

Energy is needed to break chemical bonds in molecules. This is because energy is required to pull apart atoms that want to stick together.

Energy is given out when new bonds are formed.

This is because the atoms want to stick together.

The diagram shows that the amount of chemical energy in carbon dioxide and water is less than the chemical energy in methane and oxygen. The difference represents the energy given out as heat when methane burns (remember that energy cannot be created or destroyed).

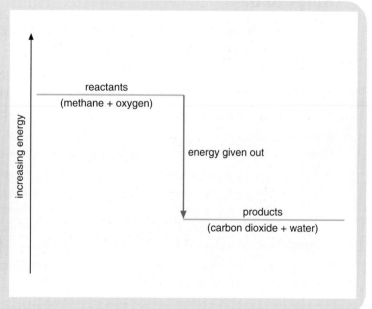

Activation energy

Remember that methane does not just burst into flames as soon as it mixes with air. A spark or flame is needed to supply some energy to break the first few chemical bonds and start the reaction. After that, the reaction provides enough energy to keep going.

This 'starting energy' is called **activation energy**. A more detailed **energy level diagram** can be drawn to include the effect of activation energy.

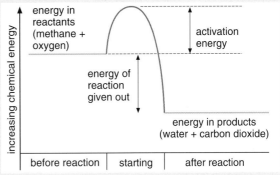

An energy level diagram for an exothermic reaction.

Exothermic or endothermic (SS) BB3, BB4

Most chemical reactions are **exothermic**: they give out energy, usually as heat but sometimes also as light, sound or electrical energy.

Some reactions are **endothermic**: energy is taken in as the reaction proceeds. For endothermic reactions, the chemical energy in the final products is greater than in the starting materials.

In most of the chemical reactions you will study, the total number of chemical bonds that have to be broken to split up the starting materials will equal the number of new bonds formed as the products are made. If the new bonds are stronger than the old ones, the reaction is exothermic. If the products contain weaker bonds than the starting materials, the reaction is endothermic.

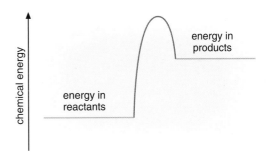

An energy level diagram for an endothermic reaction.

? Things to do

1   Chemistry data books list the energy needed to break different kinds of bonds. An equal amount of energy is given out if the same type of bond is formed from separate atoms. When methane burns, all of the bonds in methane and oxygen must be broken, so that new bonds can form.

C–H   bond energy   412 kJ

O=O   bond energy   496 kJ

C=O   bond energy   743 kJ

O–H   bond energy   463 kJ

Use these values to calculate the energy change when methane burns.

2   Ethanol, propanol and butanol are all liquid fuels. Write a plan for an investigation to compare the energy given out when each fuel burns. Say what you would have to measure and how you would work out your answer.

4 What joins atoms together?

All atoms are made of a tiny nucleus, surrounded by electrons. Only the outermost electrons are involved in bonding atoms together. Non-metal elements link with each other by sharing electrons. Bonds formed in this way are called **covalent bonds**.

In methane, the central carbon atom has four electrons in its outermost layer. Each one of these pairs up with an electron from a hydrogen atom. This forms four **single covalent bonds**. The shared electron pair are attracted by both the nucleus of the carbon atom and the nucleus of the hydrogen atom. It is this attraction that holds the atoms together.

The electrons are negatively charged and the nuclei of the atoms positively charged, so the shared pairs of electrons hold the atoms together rather like pieces of double-sided sticky tape.

A methane molecule can also be shown in a diagram where each line represents a pair of shared electrons.

Oxygen molecules consist of pairs of oxygen atoms held together by a **double covalent bond**.

Each oxygen atom contributes two electrons to be shared, so two pairs of electrons are shared and these hold the two oxygen atoms together.

Carbon dioxide and water molecules are also held together by covalent bonds, in which electrons are shared.

Very small atoms (such as hydrogen, helium, lithium) only have room for two electrons, but for all other atoms, an arrangement with eight electrons round the outside, in an 'outer layer', is particularly favourable. If you can look back to *Mining and minerals* (Y10), you can check that the arrangement in each of these examples gives each atom the most favourable number of electrons round an outer layer.

Small covalent molecules like those of water or carbon dioxide only have weak attractions for other molecules around them. Only small amounts of energy are needed to separate the molecules, so these substances have low melting and boiling points.

SS BB5

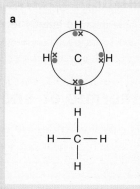

a

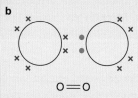

b

c

Different representations of covalent bonding in molecules.

? Things to do

1   Draw diagrams of carbon dioxide and water, using lines to represent the covalent bonds.

2   Each nitrogen atom has five electrons in its outer layer. Nitrogen atoms form three single covalent bonds with hydrogen to form ammonia (NH_3). Draw dot-and-cross and line diagrams of an ammonia molecule.

3   In nitrogen gas, nitrogen atoms are held together in pairs by a triple covalent bond. Draw dot-and-cross and line diagrams to show a nitrogen molecule (N_2).

Covalent bonds in hydrocarbons

All hydrocarbons contain covalent bonds. The simplest hydrocarbons, in which all of the bonds are single bonds, are called **alkanes**. Methane is the simplest alkane, the next simplest member of the family is **ethane**.

Carbon can easily form strong bonds to other carbon atoms and it is this which makes it possible to build up a whole series of alkanes, some with very long chains of carbon atoms.

Check carefully to see that each carbon atom has eight electrons round the outside.

The next member of the alkane family is propane. Again, check that each carbon atom has eight outside electrons in this molecule.

Alkanes are said to be **saturated** (because there are no electrons unused which could 'soak up' any more atoms into the molecule).

Alkenes

It is also possible for a carbon atom to form a double covalent bond to another carbon atom (each atom contributes two electrons to be shared). Hydrocarbons with a double carbon–carbon bond are called **alkenes**.

Alkenes are very reactive because this double bond is easily broken open, leaving just a single bond between the carbon atoms, and releasing an electron on each carbon atom which can be used to link on another atom.

As extra atoms can be added on, these reactions are called **addition reactions**. Because alkenes can absorb extra atoms in this way they are said to be **unsaturated**.

![question mark icon]

Things to do

4 The molecular formula of propane is C_3H_8. Draw dot-and-cross and line diagrams of the alkanes with **a** four carbon atoms **b** five carbon atoms in each molecule, and so work out the formula of each alkane.

5 Draw a line diagram to show the bonding in propene, an alkene with three carbon atoms. What is it's molecular formula?

6 Ethene reacts with bromine (Br_2) by an addition reaction. Draw a line diagram to show the structure of the molecule (called dibromoethane) which is formed.

5 Ionic bonding

SS **BB6, BB7**

Atoms of non-metal elements have outer layers of electrons which are nearly complete. They can fill the remaining spaces by sharing electrons with other non-metal atoms.

Atoms of metallic elements have only a few electrons in the outer layer. They cannot build up a full set by sharing. However, metals can react with non-metals. The few outer electrons from the metal atom are transferred to the non-metal. Each atom then has a stable arrangement of electrons similar to that in a noble gas.

Common salt, sodium chloride, is an example of a compound formed in this way. Each sodium atom has just one outer electron. If this is given away, the atom is left with a stable arrangement like that in the noble gas neon.

Each chlorine atom has seven outer electrons. If one electron is gained from sodium, the chlorine has a full set of eight, like the noble gas argon.

Of course, the sodium atom still has its original 11 protons, but now has only 10 electrons, so the atom has a positive charge (the chlorine has one extra electron, so has a negative charge). Atoms or groups with an electric charge are called **ions**.

The opposite charges on the ions mean that they are held together by electrical attraction. This is called **ionic bonding**.

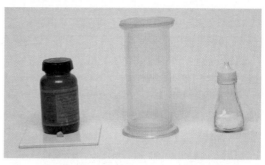

When sodium and chlorine combine they form sodium chloride, or salt.

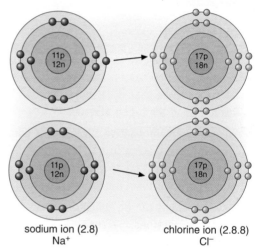

sodium ion (2.8)
Na⁺

chlorine ion (2.8.8)
Cl⁻

An electron is transferred from the sodium to the chlorine atom in the formation of sodium chloride (NaCl).

Covalent bonding only attracts the two atoms which form the bond. Bonds within a molecule are strong, but forces between molecules are weak, so they are easily separated.

The electrical attraction of ionic bonding acts in all directions. Each sodium ion attracts all chlorine ions anywhere near it. Each chlorine ion attracts all nearby sodium ions.

The whole crystal lattice is strongly held together. A lot of energy is needed to break the ions free, so ionic compounds have high melting points.

When an ionic substance is melted, the ions are free to move. The liquid can conduct electricity.

Water molecules are small enough to get between ions, and weaken the attraction between them, so ionic solids often dissolve in water. In the solution, the ions are free to move, so the solution conducts electricity.

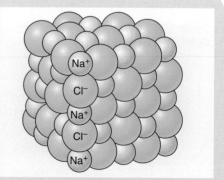

Pure sodium chloride forms crystals with a strong crystal lattice (Na⁺Cl⁻).

What holds atoms together in metals?

All metals conduct electricity. This means that there are charged particles that can move through the metal. These charged particles are electrons.

When a piece of metal conducts electricity, the outer electrons of the atoms move through the metal. A metal atom without its outer electrons becomes a positively charged ion.

You can think of a metal as a giant structure of positively charged metal ions with negatively charged electrons spread between the ions holding them together.

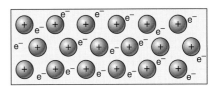

Electrons move through a metal as it conducts electricity.

Different arrangements in carbon (SS) BB8

Carbon can exist in two different covalent giant structures. One form is **diamond**. Diamond:

● is very hard.
● does not conduct electricity.

This suggests that all the atoms are held together very strongly and with no charged particles that are free to move.

In a diamond structure each carbon atom has four outer electrons and can form four covalent bonds with other atoms. This then continues throughout the structure. It is a very strong structure with a very high melting point.

The other form of carbon is **graphite**. Graphite:

● is soft and slippery.
● conducts electricity.

This suggests that parts of the structure are not held strongly to each other, so they can slide past each other.

The carbon atoms are arranged in flat layers. Each atom is held to three other carbon atoms by covalent bonds. The fourth electron is able to move. This explains why graphite, even though it is a non-metal, can conduct electricity.

The layers of carbon atoms have only weak bonds between them. They will move over each other. This is why graphite is slippery.

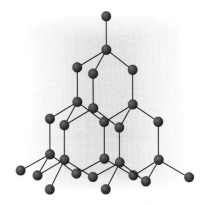

The crystal structure of diamond.

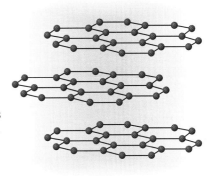

The crystal structure of graphite.

? Things to do

1 Magnesium (2 outer electrons) reacts with oxygen (6 outer electrons) by ionic bonding.

 a Draw diagrams similar to the ones above to show how many electrons are transferred

 b What is the charge on i a magnesium ion ii an oxygen ion?

 c Suggest why magnesium oxide (m. pt. 2800 °C) has a higher melting point than sodium chloride (800 °C)

2 Use atomic models to make models of diamond and graphite.

3 Explain why diamond has a high melting point even though it contains covalent bonds.

6 A great name in chemical history

Sir Humphry Davy

All chemical substances are made up from just a few (about 100) elements. One of the most important ideas in chemistry was to find ways of arranging the elements which would reveal patterns in their properties and so make it easier to forecast new reactions. A great problem in the past was that not all of the elements were known. Searching for patterns was like doing a jigsaw with pieces missing!

Humphry Davy did much important scientific work, including the discovery of new elements.

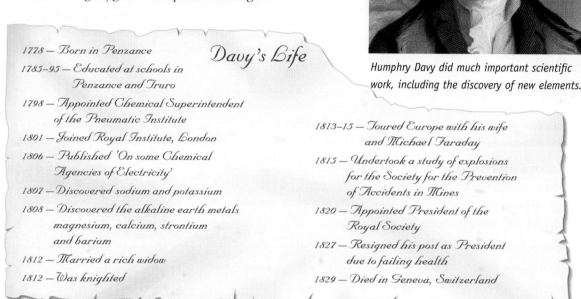

Davy's Life

1778 – Born in Penzance

1785–95 – Educated at schools in Penzance and Truro

1798 – Appointed Chemical Superintendent of the Pneumatic Institute

1801 – Joined Royal Institute, London

1806 – Published 'On some Chemical Agencies of Electricity'

1807 – Discovered sodium and potassium

1808 – Discovered the alkaline earth metals magnesium, calcium, strontium and barium

1812 – Married a rich widow

1812 – Was knighted

1813–15 – Toured Europe with his wife and Michael Faraday

1815 – Undertook a study of explosions for the Society for the Prevention of Accidents in Mines

1820 – Appointed President of the Royal Society

1827 – Resigned his post as President due to failing health

1829 – Died in Geneva, Switzerland

Experimenter extraordinaire

Davy's first job was as Chemical Superintendent of the Pneumatic Institute. Pneumatic means 'of the air', and the Institute was founded to study different gases.

Davy tested nitrous oxide on himself and noticed that he could no longer feel his toothache. He had discovered the anaesthetic properties of the gas. However, it was not until 50 years later that the gas was used when extracting teeth.

Davy took even more risks experimenting on himself by inhaling water gas. He nearly died as a result – which is not surprising when you realise that water gas is a mixture of steam and carbon monoxide!

Elementary discoveries

When Davy first began work at the Royal Institute he concentrated on the new subject of electrochemistry. A device to produce an electric current, the first electric cell, had recently been invented. It was called Volta's pile, and was made of alternate zinc and silver discs, separated by damp paper.

Davy thought that the electric current arose from chemical combinations between the zinc and silver. He wondered if the process could be reversed – could an electric current be used to break down substances?

Davy tried out his idea on a variety of substances. By 1807 he had developed his method sufficiently to be able to decompose soda and potash (sodium carbonate and potassium carbonate). He called the soft silvery metals that he obtained 'sodium' and 'potassium'.

The following year he discovered strontium and barium, and then magnesium and calcium. In two years he had discovered six new elements!

Davy was an enthusiastic experimenter, who thought nothing of persuading his friends Robert Southey and Samuel Taylor Coleridge (both famous poets) to inhale nitrous oxide. As it happened, this was not too risky, but Davy did not know this!

The Davy lamp

Davy is most famous for inventing the Davy safety lamp. It was the result of research that he carried out for the Society for the Prevention of Accidents in Mines.

A gas called firedamp (now known as methane) builds up in coal mines. Miners used naked candles to work by, and the candles sometimes ignited pockets of firedamp, causing explosions.

Davy knew they could not cover the candles with glass because a flame needs oxygen to burn. Also, he discovered that firedamp only ignited above a certain temperature. After some experiments he came up with an idea for a design for a lamp.

The lamp had a double layer of metal gauze around the flame. The gauze let the air in so the flame would continue to burn. It also let the firedamp in, which would also burn. But it conducted the heat away so that the firedamp outside the lamp was not heated to its ignition temperature and so did not explode.

Although England and France were at war, Davy visited Napoleon's court and he and his wife were presented to the Emperor.

The Davy lamp was very successful. After its introduction the number of explosions in mines was greatly reduced.

Other interests

When Davy was President of the Royal Society he became one of the founders of the Zoological Society. He persuaded the new society to set up a Zoological Gardens in Regents Park – this is now London Zoo.

Davy lamps were still used long after battery operated lamps were introduced. The shape of the flame indicated the levels (dangerous or safe) of firedamp present.

Before the Periodic Table was devised chemists were looking for patterns in properties of elements and their compounds.

The shape of the Periodic Table was worked out by:

● putting elements in order of increasing mass of their atoms. Hydrogen with the lightest atoms was put first.

● starting new lines so that elements with similar properties were put into the same vertical column.

These vertical columns were called **groups**.

Much later chemists realised that atoms were made up of protons, neutrons and electrons. The elements could then be arranged in order of the number of protons in the nucleus of each atom. This number is called **atomic number**. This is the same as the number of electrons in the atom.

If you look at the electron arrangements you will notice that the electrons in the atoms of the first 20 elements are arranged in four **shells**, or layers. The first shell contains electrons with the lowest energy. It can hold a maximum of two electrons. The second and third shells can hold eight electrons.

The arrangement of electrons found in noble gases, for example helium, neon, argon is particularly stable and these elements are very unreactive.

For example helium, which has very low density, is used to fill airships and balloons. It is much safer to use than hydrogen, which is flammable. Argon is used to fill light bulbs. Convection currents in the gas carry away energy to stop the filament overheating. Because it is unreactive, there is no chemical attack on the filament.

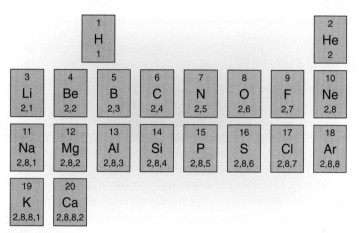

The first 20 elements in the Periodic Table.

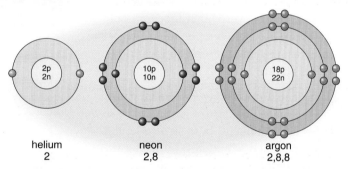

The electron arrangement for the noble gases helium, neon and argon.

? Things to do

1   Look up the atomic number (proton number) and relative atomic mass of argon and potassium. Think about the properties of these elements compared to other elements in Group 0 and Group I. Which gives the correct order in the table – proton number or atomic mass?

2   Suggest why argon atoms are heavier than potassium atoms even though they contain fewer protons and electrons.

Explaining some patterns in the Periodic Table

The elements in Group 0 of the Periodic Table are called noble gases. They are all unreactive gases. Their unreactivity can be explained because the atoms of these are elements have filled outer shells/layers and this leads to stability.

In a similar way other patterns in the Periodic Table can be explained.

Neon gas at low pressure glows red when an electric current is passed through it.

Group I

The alkali metals in Group I react in a similar way but increase in reactivity down the group. They all have a single electron in the outer shell. When they react the atom of the element loses this outer shell electron and forms an ion. For example:

$$Na \rightarrow Na^+ + e^-$$

The electrons are held in the atom by the positively charged nucleus. So an outer electron will be more easily removed from a large atom than a small atom.

Another factor is the effect of electrons in inner shells/layers. These inner electrons repel the outer electron and make it more easily lost. This is called **shielding**.

For these two reasons, potassium is more reactive than sodium which, in turn, is more reactive than lithium.

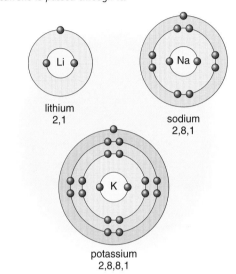

Electron configurations for lithium, sodium and potassium.

Group VII

The halogens in Group VII increase in reactivity up the group. When halogen atoms react they gain an electron in the outer shell/layer forming a negatively charged ion. For example:

$$F + e^- \rightarrow F^-$$

This electron will be gained more readily by a small atom because the electron will be closer to the nucleus of the atom and so held more strongly. Again shielding has an effect. In larger atoms, the approaching electron is repelled by the inner shells of electrons making the formation of the ion more difficult.

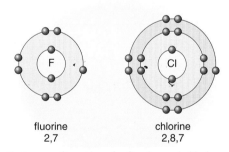

Electron configurations for fluorine and chlorine.

? Things to do

3   Find the elements beryllium (Be), magnesium (Mg) and calcium (Ca).

   a In which group of the Periodic Table are these elements placed?

   b Write down the electron arrangements of atoms of these three elements.

   c Predict the order of reactivity of these elements.

   d Explain why there is a difference in the reactivity of these elements.

Elements which have similar chemical properties are found in the same **group**, or column of the Periodic Table.

Group I (SS) BB9

The elements in Group I include lithium (Li), sodium (Na) and potassium (K). They are all soft metals that are shiny when freshly cut but rapidly tarnish in air. They are all reactive metals. They react with cold water to form hydrogen gas and leave an alkaline solution. For example:

sodium + water → sodium hydroxide + hydrogen.

$$2 Na + 2 H_2O \rightarrow 2 NaOH + H_2$$

These metals in Group I are called **alkali metals**. All alkali metals react in a similar way but they become more reactive down the group.

- The order of reactivity is: Li<Na<K

Heat from the reaction melts the sodium ...

Group VII (SS) BB10

The elements in Group VII are reactive non-metals. These include fluorine (F), chlorine (Cl), bromine (Br) and iodine (I) They all react with sodium metal to form similar compounds.

fluorine + sodium → sodium fluoride	$F_2 + 2Na \rightarrow 2NaF$
chlorine + sodium → sodium chloride	$Cl_2 + 2Na \rightarrow 2NaCl$
bromine + sodium → sodium bromide	$Br_2 + 2Na \rightarrow 2NaBr$
iodine + sodium → sodium iodide	$I_2 + 2Na \rightarrow 2NaI$

... the hydrogen formed catches fire ...

These sodium compounds formed are all white crystalline solids. They have high melting points and are soluble in water. They contain ionic bonding.

Sodium fluoride, sodium chloride, sodium bromide and sodium iodide are all salts. The family of elements in Group VII are called **halogens**. The word halogen comes from the Greek for 'salt producing'.

Unlike the alkali metals, the halogens become less reactive as you go down the group.

- The order of reactivity is: F>Cl>Br>I

... the flame is coloured yellow by sodium atoms.

Displacement reactions of halogens

The differences in the reactivity of halogens can be shown by displacement reactions where one halogen displaces another which is less reactive from a sodium salt. For example, if chlorine is bubbled through a solution of sodium bromide, a red solution is formed. The red colour is due to the formation of bromine, pushed out by the more reactive chlorine.

sodium bromide + chlorine → sodium chloride + bromine

$$2NaBr + Cl_2 \rightarrow 2NaCl + Br_2$$

A similar reaction would take place if chlorine was added to sodium iodide.

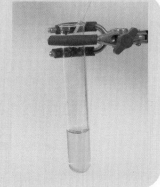

When sodium chloride solution is added to silver nitrate solution a white precipitate (solid) of silver chloride is formed.

silver nitrate + sodium chloride → silver chloride + sodium nitrate

$$AgNO_3 \quad + \quad NaCl \quad \rightarrow \quad AgCl \quad + \quad NaNO_3$$

Similar reactions occur if sodium bromide or sodium iodide are added to silver nitrate. The silver bromide forms as a cream precipitate and silver iodide as a yellow precipitate.

The silver halides are light sensitive. For example, the white silver chloride in the test tube quickly turns purplish, especially in a sunny laboratory. This is because the silver chloride is splitting up into silver and chlorine.

The clouds of white particles of silver chloride are forming as sodium chloride solution is added to silver nitrate solution.

Transition metals

The transition metals form a large block of elements placed between Groups II and III in the Periodic Table.

These metals include manganese, chromium, iron and nickel as well as the metals copper, silver and gold which are used in coins and jewellery.

They are much denser and less reactive than alkali metals. Notice that many of the compounds formed by transition metals are coloured.

Photographic film is coated with silver halides. When exposed to light, silver is formed and darkens the film.

Most transition metals can form two (or more) different types of compounds, depending on how many electrons they give away. For example, iron can form both iron (II) and iron (III) compounds. These metals can act as catalysts for reactions. They switch backwards and forwards between different types of compound as electrons are transferred in the reaction. For example, iron is used as catalyst in production of ammonia from nitrogen and hydrogen, and vanadium pentoxide is used as the catalyst in the Contact process for making sulphuric acid.

Transition metals readily form alloys (mixtures of metals). Brass (copper and zinc) is used for plumbing fittings, stainless steel (iron alloyed with chromium and nickel) is very resistant to corrosion.

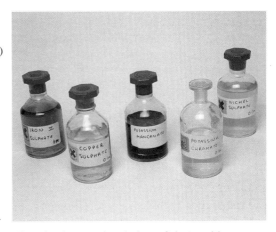

These bottles contain solutions of the transition elements, such as copper (II) sulphate (blue) and potassium manganate (VII) (purple).

? Things to do

1 Rubidium (Rb) is an alkali metal below potassium in Group I of the Periodic Table.

   a In which period is rubidium?

   b How many electrons are there in the outer shell of a rubidium atom?

   c Write word and symbol equations for the reaction of rubidium and cold water.

   d How does the reactivity of rubidium compare with lithium, sodium and potassium?

2 Write word and symbol equations for the reaction when silver nitrate and sodium bromide solutions are mixed.

1   A hair curler uses butane, C_4H_{10}, as a fuel. The butane is stored under pressure as a liquid. When the curler is switched on, butane is released and changes to a gas. The gas is ignited by a spark.

   a   At normal atmospheric pressure butane boils at $0\,°C$. Explain why it has such a low boiling point.

   b   Using lines for bonds, draw a molecule of butane. What type of bonds hold the atoms together? Using dots and crosses explain how these bonds are formed.

   c   Draw an energy level diagram to show the energy changes that occur when butane burns. Explain why a spark is needed to start the butane burning.

2   Lithium oxide, Li_2O, contains ionic bonding.

   a   Write down the electron arrangements of lithium and oxygen atoms.

   b   Explain changes in electron arrangement that occur when lithium burns in oxygen.

   c   Describe and explain the properties of lithium oxide.

3   Graphite is a solid which conducts electricity and is used in pencils.

   Poly(ethene) is a solid which is easily softened by heating and moulded into different shapes. It does not conduct electricity.

   Copper is a solid which can be drawn out into wires which are flexible but strong and which will conduct electricity.

   Use theories of bonding and structure to explain the differences between these solids and how their uses depend on their properties. Use diagrams to help you make your answer clear.

4   A group of students was asked to investigate a white crystalline solid. They found that it had the following properties:

   • soluble in water
   • insoluble in hexane
   • the solution in water was a good conductor of electricity
   • it could not be melted with a Bunsen burner.

   a   Explain how this evidence provides clues about the type of bonding in the solid.

   b   The teacher then told them that it contained a metal M with atomic number 20 and a non-metal X with atomic number 17. Draw the electronic structures of these two elements and then explain how the elements are bonded together in the solid.

   c   Explain what you would expect to happen if the students could have heated the solid to a sufficiently high temperature to melt it, and then passed a direct electric current through it.

5   In 1829, a chemist called Dobereiner noticed several examples where three elements formed a group with very similar properties. He called these triads. Each of the pairs of elements below represent two of the three members of a triad. Use the Periodic Table to suggest which was the third element, with properties in-between the two given:

   a   lithium and potassium

   b   calcium and barium

   c   chlorine and iodine

   d   sulphur and tellurium.

6   Anita says that when a candle burns in air its mass decreases.

   a   Describe how this apparatus could be used to show whether this is true.

   b   How can you explain any change of mass that occurs?

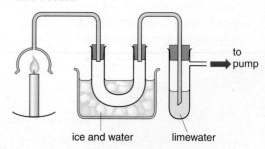

ice and water   limewater

7   Find examples of where transition metals or transition metal compounds act as catalysts.

INTRODUCING
Energy today and tomorrow

Try these first

1 What fuels are used widely for heating houses in the UK?

2 Coal is largely carbon. What is produced when coal burns in a plentiful supply of air?

3 Coal, oil and gas are three fossil fuels. How were they formed by slow natural processes?

4 Name a renewable source of energy. How is it used to make electricity?

5 Energy resources can be grouped into secondary or primary energy sources. Group the following:

coal   gas   electricity

wind   nuclear fuel

This power station uses natural wind energy to make electricity.

Electricity is distributed through the National Grid.

In this unit you will learn:

- we use energy in many different ways
- fuels can be fossil fuels (gas, coal and oil)
- electricity (a secondary fuel) can be made using many different primary fuels or energy sources
- coal-fired power stations produce air pollution and have low efficiency
- electricity can be produced by nuclear fission and possibly by nuclear fusion
- there are alternative energy resources that can be developed – some are renewable
- electricity can be generated by electromagnetic induction
- electricity generated in power stations is transported via the National Grid
- the voltage of electricity can be changed using a transformer
- electrical energy can be converted into kinetic energy in an electric motor
- the difference between alternating current and direct current.

1 Making use of energy

In a developed country like the United Kingdom large amounts of energy are needed. Most of this comes from concentrated energy sources called **fossil fuels**: coal, natural gas and oil. These are sometimes called **non-renewable** energy resources, because the processes by which they were formed take millions of years to complete. We cannot simply make more coal to replace what we use.

A smaller but growing amount of energy comes from **renewable sources** and energy is also obtained from nuclear fuel – such as uranium. This is necessary as deposits of fossil fuels are likely to run out in the near future.

All of the fuels used in the pictures except electricity are **primary fuels**. Electricity is called a **secondary** fuel because it is usually made from other fuels.

Notice the difference between these two pie charts. Much of the coal and oil is turned into electricity. There are an increasing number of power stations that turn natural gas into electricity.

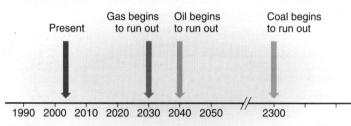

Estimated dates when fossil fuels will run out at present rates of use.

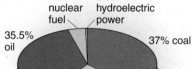

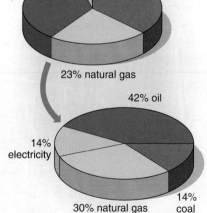

These pie charts show which primary fuels are needed to provide fuels to the consumer.

Things to do

1   Look at the picture above. What fuel is being used here?

2   How might lighting a room, making a hot drink, and doing the washing have been done 200 years ago? What fuels might have been used?

3   Suggest ways in which we can ensure that fossil fuels, such as gas, oil and coal, last longer than the times shown on the time line.

Making electricity ET1, ET2, ET3

Electricity is a very important energy resource. It is easily converted to produce heat, light, sound, movement or magnetic effects. It is also easily transported to where it is needed. Large-scale production of electricity depends on an effect discovered by Michael Faraday in the 1830s. It is called **electromagnetic induction**.

Faraday used a loop of wire to make a circuit. When the wire was moved in a magnetic field, he detected an electric current in the circuit. Moving the wire through the magnetic field had **induced** a voltage.

To produce a continuous supply of electricity, continuous movement is needed. This can be done by rotating a flat coil between the magnetic poles.

One side of the coil moves up through the magnetic field, the other moves down. Currents are induced in both sides.

At this moment, the sides of the coil are moving parallel to the magnetic field. No current is induced.

The two sides are now moving back across the field. The induced current is now in the opposite direction round the coil.

As the coil rotates, the electric current keeps changing direction – it is an **alternating current** (a.c.). To avoid the leads to the coil becoming twisted, two slip rings and 'brushes' are used to make the electrical connections to the coil.

You can make the current bigger by:

● using stronger magnets
● using a coil with more turns
● winding the coil on a soft-iron core to increase the magnetic field strength (as in an electromagnet)
● turning the coil faster (If you turn the coil faster the frequency of the alternating current will also increase.)

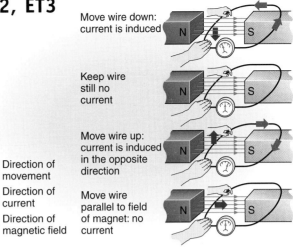

Key
➡ Direction of movement
➡ Direction of current
→ Direction of magnetic field

Move wire down: current is induced

Keep wire still no current

Move wire up: current is induced in the opposite direction

Move wire parallel to field of magnet: no current

Electromagnetic induction was first demonstrated and described by Michael Faraday.

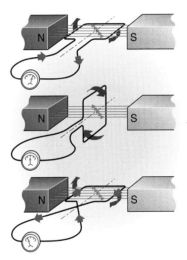

A rotating coil provides a continuous supply of electricity.

? Things to do

4 For this activity you will need to talk to someone who is over 70 years old. Ask them what things were like when they were your age.

  a What fuel was used to warm their home?

  b Was every room heated? If not, which rooms were heated?

  c Did they have hot running water? If not, how did they heat water when they needed it?

  d What fuel was used for cooking food?

5 Describe how the electric current produced from a generator is different from that produced by a torch battery.

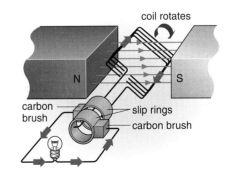

coil rotates

carbon brush

slip rings
carbon brush

In practice 'slip rings' and 'brushes' replace leads so that the coil can rotate freely.

SS ET4

A power station is a factory for making electricity. Many large power stations burn coal as the source of energy. The large main building contains furnaces, turbines and generators.

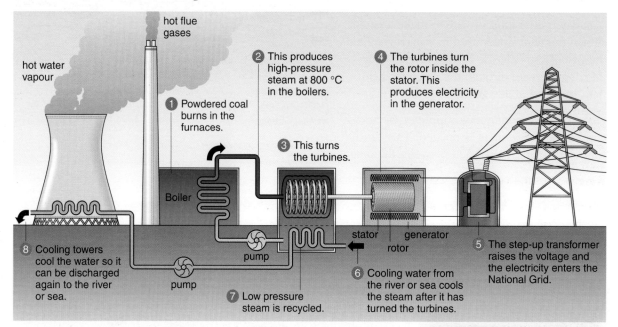

hot flue gases

hot water vapour

② This produces high-pressure steam at 800 °C in the boilers.

④ The turbines turn the rotor inside the stator. This produces electricity in the generator.

① Powdered coal burns in the furnaces.

③ This turns the turbines.

Boiler

stator   generator
          rotor

⑧ Cooling towers cool the water so it can be discharged again to the river or sea.

pump

pump

⑦ Low pressure steam is recycled.

⑥ Cooling water from the river or sea cools the steam after it has turned the turbines.

⑤ The step-up transformer raises the voltage and the electricity enters the National Grid.

The flow diagram shows how electricity is supplied through the National Grid.

Coal travels up a conveyor belt and into the power station. Here it is ground to powder and then blown into the furnaces. The powdered coal burns very quickly and produces a high temperature. This turns water in the boilers into steam. By keeping the pressure high, the steam is heated to over 800 °C.

The high pressure steam is used to turn **turbines**. Turbines are like specially designed windmills. A large number of thin blades are connected like spokes to an axle. The steam hits these blades from one side. As it passes through the gap, it makes the blades and axle spin. The spinning turbine shaft is used to turn the moving coil, or **rotor**, of a generator, producing electricity.

The generator is similar to the one that was described on the previous page. However, the current generated is very large and the sparking at the brushes would be too great. So, the magnet is rotated and the coil is kept stationary. The coil (called the **stator**) is wound on a fixed iron frame, with a rotating electromagnet (the **rotor**) in the middle. The current to the electromagnet has to be supplied using brushes , but this current is quite small. As the rotor spins, it induces an alternating current in the stator coil.

The current produced has a frequency of 50 hertz because the coil is fixed to turn at exactly 50 turns per second.

A turbine open for inspection. Note the many rows of blades.

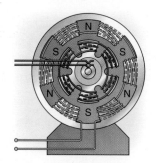

The generator in cross-section shows the magnet rotating inside the coil.

How efficient is a coal-fired power station?

How much of the energy released when the coal is burnt is transferred to electricity?

The hot flue gases from the furnaces carry some energy away. This goes up the chimneys and is wasted.

The most important energy loss, however, is in the turbines. Once the steam has passed through the blades it is cooled, to reduce its pressure and make it condense. This cooling stage is essential, because it is the **pressure difference** between the steam entering the turbine and the steam leaving it that makes the turbine turn.

The steam is cooled by water, usually taken from a nearby river. The energy transferred to the cooling water makes it hot. It must be cooled before it is returned to the river. This is the reason for the large **cooling towers** at a power station. The white fumes around the tops of the cooling towers are steam (from the hot cooling water), not smoke.

Because of these energy losses, a power station is around 35% efficient. This is not because the power station is badly designed. There is a limit to the maximum efficiency possible.

These large towers in a coal-fired power station are used to cool water.

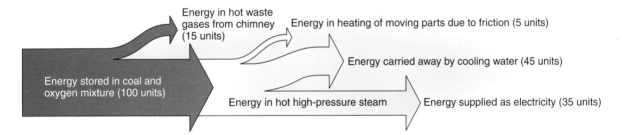

Energy in hot waste gases from chimney (15 units)

Energy in heating of moving parts due to friction (5 units)

Energy carried away by cooling water (45 units)

Energy stored in coal and oxygen mixture (100 units)

Energy in hot high-pressure steam

Energy supplied as electricity (35 units)

Are all power stations the same?

Some power stations burn oil or natural gas, instead of coal. They are very similar to coal-fired stations, but the boiler design is slightly different.

Nuclear power stations use the energy from radioactive decay of uranium atoms to provide the heat energy. The turbines and generators are similar to those in coal-fired stations.

Hydro-electric power stations also have turbines and generators, but these are turned directly by moving water, not by steam.

The first public electricity supply, for street lights in Godalming, Surrey, was supplied in 1881 from a generator installed in a watermill on the River Wey.

? Things to do

1   Why is the coal powdered before it is burnt?
2   Where is the major cause of pollution from the power station? Neil says it is from the large cooling towers. Is this true?
3   Draw a pie chart to show where the energy from burning 100 units of coal goes.

Electricity is **transmitted** from power stations to the consumers in a network of cables and wires called the **National Grid**. This moves electricity around the country from where it is produced to where it is needed.

The wires of the National Grid are made of very good conductors, but even so, they do have some resistance. Whenever there is an electric current in a cable, some of the energy is transferred to heat, overcoming the resistance of the cable.

If a current of I amps flows in a cable with resistance R watts, the energy converted to heat will be I^2R joules. To keep this energy loss to a minimum, the current should be kept as small as possible.

Pylons and transmission lines form part of the National Grid.

The rate of transfer of energy through the supply is given by current times voltage ($V \times I$). So, the higher the voltage, the smaller the current which is needed.

To reduce energy losses in the grid cables, electricity is transmitted at very high voltage.

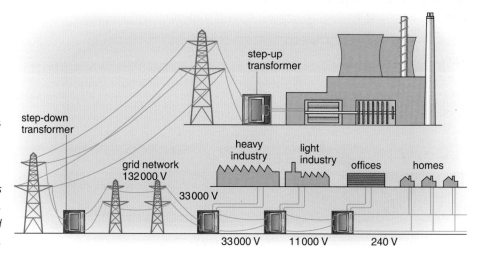

step-up transformer

step-down transformer

heavy industry

light industry

offices

homes

grid network 132 000 V

33 000 V

33 000 V

11 000 V

240 V

? Things to do

1   The picture shows a bicycle dynamo. It is a small, portable generator. Write a simple explanation of how the dynamo works.

2   A remote farm must be supplied with 10 kW of electricity. The resistance of the grid cable is 10 Ω.

   a What current is needed if the supply voltage is 100 V? (Use $I = \frac{V}{R}$)

   b What would be the power loss at 100 V? (the power loss in the cables = I^2R).

   c Now repeat the calculation at 100 000 V.

   d What is the advantage of using high voltages?

   e Are there any disadvantages transporting electricity at very high voltages?

   f Cables are usually carried overhead using pylons rather than underground. What are the advantages and disadvantages of underground cables?

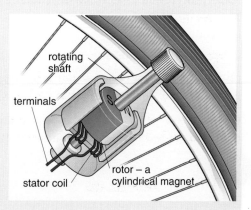

rotating shaft

terminals

stator coil

rotor – a cylindrical magnet

Changing the voltage ET5, ET6, ET7

Efficient transfer of electricity to consumers depends on using very high voltages. Fortunately, it is much easier to change the voltage of **a.c.** (alternating current) than **d.c.** (direct current) electricity.

As in the generator, the method makes use of electromagnetic induction. A brief pulse of current can be produced by moving a magnet into a coil. There is another pulse, in the opposite direction, when you pull the magnet out again.

This also works if you use an electromagnet instead of a bar magnet. Now, there is no need for anything to move. The magnetic field can be changed by switching the electromagnet on and off. When you switch the electromagnet on, there is a brief pulse of current in the secondary circuit. When you switch the electromagnet off again, there is another brief pulse of current in the opposite direction.

Current is induced in the secondary circuit when the current is **changing** in the primary circuit. An **alternating current** is always changing in size and direction. If we use an alternating current in the primary circuit, it induces another alternating current in the secondary circuit.

In a **transformer** the two coils are wound on the same iron core, so that changes in the magnetic field of the primary coil are efficiently carried to the secondary coil. Since all the wires are insulated from one another, the only link is the changing magnetic field in the core. There are two sorts of transformer – the **step-up transformer** which changes to higher voltage and the **step-down transformer**. In a step-up transformer there are more turns on the secondary coil than on the primary coil. In a step-down transformer there are more turns on the primary coil than on the secondary.

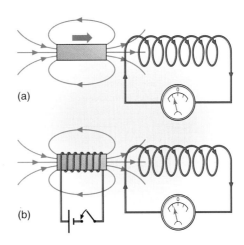
(a)

(b)

Electric current induced by a bar magnet (a) and an electromagnet (b).

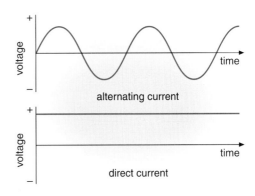

alternating current

direct current

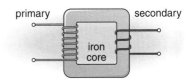

A step-down transformer.

This fits a formula:

$$\frac{\text{secondary voltage}}{\text{primary voltage}} = \frac{\text{number of turns on secondary coil}}{\text{number of turns on primary coil}}$$

A step-up transformer is used at the power station to raise the voltage. At the end of the grid lines, step down transformers are used to change it back again to the values used by industry and domestic consumers.

 Things to do

1   A local sub-station steps down the supply voltage from 11 000 volts to 230 volts. If the primary coil of the transformer has 550 turns, how many turns must the secondary coil have?

In a generator, movement (of a magnet or a coil) is used to generate an electric current. The reverse of this effect is used in electric motors.

Electricity makes movement

 ET8–10

You may remember from *Communicating information* (Y10) that an electric current in a wire causes a magnetic field round the wire. This effect is used in electromagnets.

If an electric current passes through a wire which is near to a magnet, the two magnetic fields (one from the magnet, one from the wire) interact.

The result of this can be shown using a wire 'rider' as part of a circuit. As the electric current flows through the rider, it causes a magnetic field. This field interacts with the field from the magnets, causing a force. The 'rider' will roll along the stiff copper wires.

This shows the effect which is used in an electric motor. An electric motor is a device that uses electric current and a magnet to produce movement – it can be thought of as a generator in reverse!

Putting on a spin

A coil of the wire is placed between the poles of two flat magnets. This coil becomes like a bar magnet when a current flows in it. One face of the coil becomes a North (N) pole and the other a South (S) pole. In diagram 1, the top is N and the bottom is S. The side which is the N pole is attracted towards the S pole of the flat magnet, so the coil will turn till it is in position 2.

To make it carry on rotating, the direction of the current is changed just as the coil gets to position 2. The side of the coil which was the N pole now becomes a S pole and vice versa. The forces of attraction of the two flat magnets make the coil turn over again. If the change of current direction is every time the coil is in the upright position (position 2), it will rotate continuously.

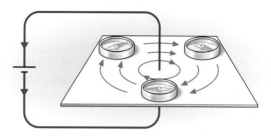

The magnetic fields from the magnet and the wire interact.

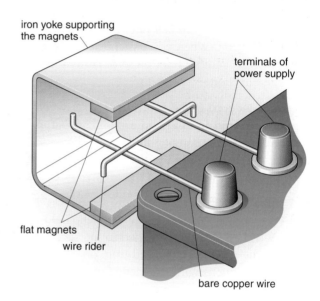

iron yoke supporting the magnets

terminals of power supply

flat magnets

wire rider

bare copper wire

The wire rider sits on the copper wires. It carries current and will slide backwards or forwards depending on the force generated.

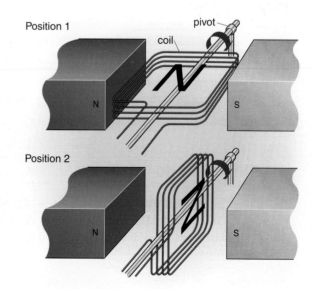

Position 1

pivot

coil

N

S

Position 2

N

S

Keeping things going

The direction of the current can be reversed every half-turn by using two brushes to supply the current. As the coil turns, each lead wire in turn will touch the brush.

To provide a smoother, more continuous contact, a split-ring is used, with one half attached to each of the leads. The coil turns, the split-ring and the leads from the electricity supply remain still.

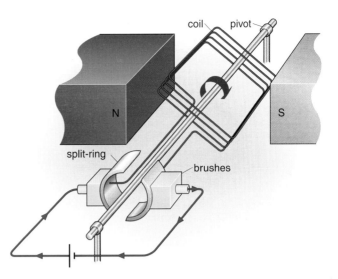

Adding power

Several things can be done to make the motor more powerful.

- put several coils at different angles round the shaft of the motor, instead of just one. This needs a more complicated split-ring (for example four coils need 8 sections on the ring), but gives smoother movement.
- use more turns on each coil
- wind the coils round a soft iron core to concentrate the magnetic field
- use an electromagnet rather than a permanent one.

A car starter motor is a direct current motor – using electric current to provide a force, or movement.

? Things to do

1   Draw a picture of a solenoid (a long coil of wire) as part of an electric circuit. Draw lines to indicate the magnetic field round the solenoid when the current is flowing. Indicate the direction of the current and of the magnetic field.

2   With your group make lists of all the devices you can think of which have electric motors in them:

   a in your home

   b in the school laboratory

   c in other everyday situations.

3   a Explain clearly what the split-ring arrangement is for and why it is necessary.

   b Suggest two ways of changing the direction of rotation of the coil.

   c Suggest two ways of changing the speed at which the coil rotates.

Problems with burning coal (SS) ET11, ET12

Coal is mainly carbon. Carbon burns in air to form carbon dioxide.

$$C + O_2 = CO_2$$
Carbon + oxygen = carbon dioxide

Carbon dioxide in the atmosphere absorbs radiation. This contributes to the **greenhouse effect** (see *Restless Earth*, Y10). Increased amounts of carbon dioxide in the atmosphere could contribute to **global warming**, changing the balance of nature in ways which are difficult to predict. Because of this, there is pressure to reduce the amount of fossil fuel which is burnt.

Coal also contains sulphur. This burns to form sulphur dioxide.

$$S + O_2 = SO_2$$
Sulphur + oxygen = sulphur dioxide

Sulphur dioxide is a very acidic gas. Some falls to the ground near to the power station, but much may be carried long distances in the chimney fumes. It reacts with oxygen from the air and water to form sulphuric acid, which is a cause of **acid rain**.

Acid rain can cause damage to trees, dissolve out chemicals from the soil, and poison fish in rivers and lakes. Britain and other European countries have agreed to reduce emissions of sulphur dioxide. Some coal-fired stations have been fitted with **flue gas desulphurisation** (FGD) plants. The gases from the burning coal pass through a spray of powdered lime and water.

$$SO_2 + CaO = CaSO_3$$
Sulphur dioxide + lime = calcium sulphite

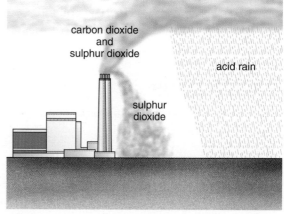

Burning coal results in the formation of acid rain, which is harmful to life.

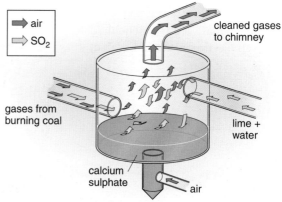

Flue gas desulphurisation plants are used to reduce emissions of sulphur dioxide and prevent acid rain.

The calcium sulphite then reacts with oxygen in the air to form calcium sulphate (gypsum), a solid which can be used to make plaster for the building trade.

$$2CaSO_3 + O_2 = 2CaSO_4$$

The lime is obtained by heating limestone, which is dug from quarries and transported to the power stations.

$$CaCO_3 = CaO + CO_2$$

Some of the electricity from the power station is used to drive the FGD process, which adds to the cost of the electricity for sale.

Burning coal also results in large amounts of ash, which also has to be disposed of.

Considering other energy sources ET13

Some power stations now burn natural gas or oil as the source of energy. However, these are both fossil fuels, which are not renewable and both form carbon dioxide when they burn.

Because of worries about global warming and acid rain, and because fossil fuels will become more expensive as they begin to run out, much attention is being given to ways of using other energy resources which are **renewable**.

Renewable energy resources

from the Earth's core	from the Sun	from the sea
The centre of the Earth is kept very hot by the decay of radioactive substances in rocks: • hot spots in the solid crust can heat water to produce steam (**geothermal energy**) which can be used to drive a turbine and generator.	Radiation reaching the Earth from the Sun: • can be used directly for heating water (**solar panels**) • is used to generate electricity directly in **solar cells** • is transferred into chemical energy by growing plants, which can be used for fuel in various ways (**biomass**) • can be trapped and converted into **biogas** • drives the Earth's weather, producing **wind** and **waves** whose energy can be harnessed. Rain collected in high lakes and reservoirs is used in **hydroelectric power stations**.	The gravitational pull of the Moon and the Sun, combined with the rotation of the Earth, produce tides: • the flow of water into or out of river estuaries as the tide rises or falls can be used to drive turbines, which then drive generators.

Energy from the Earth's core

Reykjavik, the capital of Iceland, has a lower temperature than any town in Britain. Yet the inhabitants can keep warm without burning any fossil fuels at all.

Iceland is a volcanic region and its capital is heated by natural hot water springs – central heating without burning fuel.

Even when there are no natural hot springs, there are often hot rocks under the Earth's surface.

In a geothermal power station, cold water is pumped down to the hot rocks. It seeps through cracks, getting heated up in the process. The hot water comes up a second pipe to the surface where it boils, as the pressure on it is reduced. The steam can be used to drive a turbine and generator.

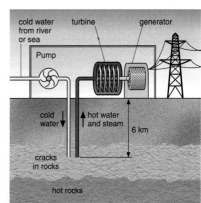

A geothermal power station produces electricity from the heat in the Earth's crust.

Is coal best for making electricity?

Energy from the Sun ET14

Solar panels

Many buildings have solar panels to trap energy from sunlight. Short wavelength infra-red radiation from sunlight is absorbed by dark pipes and heats water inside. Any longer wavelength radiation coming back from the pipes is trapped by a glass cover. The hot water from the pipes is circulated by a pump and the energy is transferred to the domestic hot water. Even on a cloudy day, a solar panel can reduce the amount of other fuels needed to provide hot water.

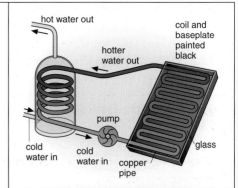

Solar cells

A solar cell is a thin sandwich of semiconductor materials. Energy from sunlight falling on the cell creates a voltage. Modern solar cells can convert about 15% of the light energy they receive into electrical energy.

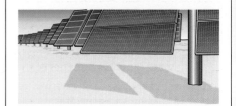

Biomass

One of the most efficient ways of trapping the Sun's energy is by growing plants. Taking the Earth as a whole, energy is being trapped by the growth of new plant material six times faster than we are using up energy in fossil fuels.

Trees and plants can be burned directly. For example, a new straw-fired power station in Cambridgeshire uses straw left over from growing cereals. In Brazil, alcohol (ethanol) is produced by **fermentation** of sugar from sugar cane. Car engines can be adapted to run on a mixture of alcohol and petrol.

Biogas

Plant and animal material can both be broken down by bacteria. When this happens in the absence of air, methane, CH_4, is formed. Vegetable waste or animal manure can be placed in airtight fermenters to produce methane which is burned for heat or to run generators.

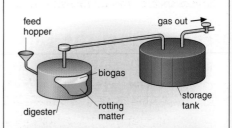

Wind energy

Energy from the Sun and rotation of the Earth produce winds. Wind turbines use the kinetic energy of the wind to drive a generator to make electricity. Six hundred of these in a 'wind farm' could provide as much electricity as a coal-fired power station.

Energy from water

Wave power

Waves carry an enormous amount of energy. The problem is how to make use of it. One idea is to use a line of nodding '**ducks**'. These would bob up and down as the waves passed. Inside each duck is a small generator, driven by the motion of the duck. Cables carry the electricity back to land. The line of ducks has to be flexible enough to move with the waves yet strong enough to withstand heavy seas.

Tidal energy

The photograph on page 189 shows a tidal barrier. The flow of the tide into or out of a river estuary drives turbines to generate electricity.

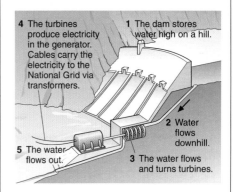

4 The turbines produce electricity in the generator. Cables carry the electricity to the National Grid via transformers.

1 The dam stores water high on a hill.

2 Water flows downhill.

5 The water flows out.

3 The water flows and turns turbines.

Hydroelectric power

The gravitational potential energy of water stored behind dams is converted to movement as the water flows down through turbines. These then turn generators to produce electricity.

Why don't we make more use of renewable energy sources?

With increasing fossil fuel prices and problems of pollution caused by burning fossil fuels, using renewable resources seems more attractive. Unfortunately, although the energy itself is 'free', collecting it can be expensive.

Tidal and hydroelectric schemes are large and expensive to set up. Although they do not pollute the air they have other environmental consequences by disturbing the natural water flow. Solar and geothermal sources can produce heating for buildings but it is hard to get high enough temperatures to generate electricity. The energy of the wind and waves is very 'spread out', or **dispersed**, – so it is hard to collect.

Scientific research is continuing in many countries to make the methods of harnessing these resources more efficient and cheaper.

? Things to do

1 A power station burning straw produces large amounts of carbon dioxide. However, it is said to be 'environmentally neutral'. Explain why.

2 Opponents of renewable fuels sometimes say that they are not available when they are needed, for example no wind on calm days or no solar power at night. Explain how these disadvantages could be overcome.

3 Make a database to store information about different energy resources. Here are some headings you might use:
  ● advantages   ● disadvantages   ● is it used to generate electricity?
  ● small scale or large scale energy source?   ● cost to maintain (high, medium or low).

In *Seeing inside the body* (Y11), you saw that reactions which change the nucleus of radioactive atoms give out a lot of energy. Some of these reactions can be used as an alternative to burning coal, gas or oil to provide the energy for power stations.

A nuclear chain reaction

Most atoms of the metal uranium contain 92 protons and 146 neutrons in the nucleus. This isotope (U-238) has mass number 238. About 7% of uranium atoms have 92 protons and just 143 neutrons. This isotope (U-235) has an unusual property. If an atom of U-235 is struck by a stray neutron, it splits into two nearly equal parts. This is known as **nuclear fission**. It gives out very large amounts of energy.

Fission also gives out 2 or 3 neutrons. If these hit other nearby U-235 atoms, **a chain reaction** is set up, in which each atom which splits sets off others to keep the process going.

In ordinary uranium, these simply escape into the surroundings. However, uranium can be enriched by removing some of the U-238 atoms. This means that the U-235 atoms are now closer together and more likely to be hit by one of the neutrons.

In a nuclear reactor, rods of enriched uranium are piled up. A shield of graphite round the 'pile' reflects neutrons back in. The neutrons strike other U-235 atoms, causing them to split too.

The chain reaction heats high pressure steam to drive the turbines in a nuclear power station. The production of electricity is the same as in an ordinary power station, but the nuclear reactor replaces the coal furnaces.

Keeping control

For nuclear reactors, the fissionable material is not made too concentrated. This makes it easier to keep the chain reaction under control.

If the fuel is made too concentrated, the reaction 'runs away' causing an explosion. This is the basis of the atomic bomb. Nuclear reactors have control rods made of a material (cadmium) which absorbs neutrons. These can be lowered into the reactor to slow or stop the chain reaction.

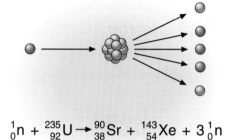

$$\,_{0}^{1}n + \,_{92}^{235}U \rightarrow \,_{38}^{90}Sr + \,_{54}^{143}Xe + 3\,_{0}^{1}n$$

The equation for the fission of U-235 after irradiation by a neutron.

A nuclear power station in the north of England.

A nuclear explosion leaves a 'mushroom cloud' effect.

Nuclear fusion

The process used in nuclear power stations involves heavy atoms splitting apart. **Nuclear fusion** can be thought of as the opposite – small, light atomic nuclei joining together.

This is the process which provides energy in the Sun and other stars. It has been possible to create this reaction on Earth, using isotopes of hydrogen (deuterium H-2, and tritium H-3)

$$^2_1H + {}^3_1H = {}^4_2He + {}^1_0n + ENERGY$$

The products are a helium atom and a neutron. Very large amounts of energy are released.

This kind of process requires very high temperatures to get it started before it can release energy. A hydrogen bomb involves a fusion reaction but a temperature of 1 000 000 °C is needed to detonate it. Research has been going on for many years but scientists are still trying to get more energy out than they have to put in to get it started.

In the JET (Joint European Torus) project, a doughnut-shaped magnetic field is used to hold hot plasma. The apparatus in the diagram is large – as high as a two-storey building. In November 1991, JET project scientists reported that they had succeeded in controlling a fusion reaction for a short time.

Research continues because, if we could get it to work reliably on a large scale, the rewards would be enormous. The fuel is hydrogen. Water contains hydrogen and there is plenty of water around.

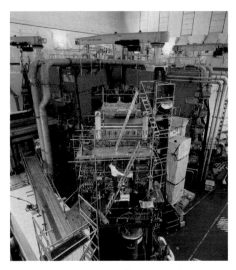

The JET project involves fusion experiments at very high temperatures.

Things to do

1 Here are some statements about nuclear power. Divide them into two columns – advantages of nuclear power and disadvantages of nuclear power.

  a There are dangers of leaks of radioactive substances.

  b Nuclear fuel saves valuable fossil fuels for other uses.

  c Nuclear fuels do not produce smoke, soot or acid rain.

  d There are risks from accidents using radioactive materials.

  e Nuclear fuels will last for another 2000 years.

  f Nuclear fuels do not produce carbon dioxide which leads to global warming.

  g Some of the waste from nuclear reactors will be reactive for hundreds of years and it is difficult to dispose of safely.

2 Use the information in question 1 to produce a poster giving a balanced view of the advantages and disadvantages of nuclear power.

1   Neil and Anita are choosing a fuel for heating their new house. Complete the table giving the advantages and disadvantages of different fuels.

Fuel	Advantages	Disadvantages
Coal		
Natural gas		
Oil		
Electricity		

2   In the UK, on average, 20 W of solar energy arrives on each square metre of land during daylight hours. A solar power station is planned to produce 20 MW of electrical power. If the panels are 10% efficient (that is, they transfer 10% of the solar energy into electrical energy), what area of solar panels is required?

3   A transistor radio can be powered by six dry cell batteries (9 V). Alternatively, it can be used from the mains. What extra devices are needed in the radio for it to be used on the mains?

4   a   What happens to a wire through which an electric current is passing when the wire is in a strong magnetic field ?

   b   Draw a diagram of an electric motor. Label **coil**, **magnet**, **split-ring** and **brushes**.

   c   Explain why the graphite brushes have to be replaced from time to time.

   d   Explain clearly what the split-ring arrangement is for and why it is necessary.

   e   Suggest two ways of changing the direction of rotation of the coil.

5   The UK government has set targets to increase the amount of electricity which is generated using renewable energy resources. Make a list of resources and discuss good and bad points related to using it on a larger scale in the UK.

6   When this magnet is pushed into the coil, the meter needle kicks momentarily to the right.

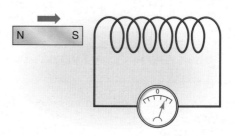

   a   Copy and complete the table below.

Action	Effect of action
magnet pushed in	meter needle kicks to the right
magnet iside the coil but not moving	
magnet pulled out	
magnet pushed in faster than before	
magnet turned round and pushed in (N first)	

   b   Write down one application of the experiment above.

7   A power station generates 25 MW of power. The power is transmitted at 400 kV

   a   What is the current in the power lines?

   b   Explain why electricity is transmitted at such a high voltage.

   c   Explain, including a diagram, how the voltage is increased before it is transmitted.

   d   Why is mains voltage an alternating current?

8   A large power station burns 200 tonnes of coal each hour. This coal contains 144 tonnes of carbon, 40 tonnes of hydrogen and 3 tonnes of sulphur. Calculate the masses of carbon dioxide, water vapour and sulphur dioxide produced each hour. [H=1; C=12; O=16]

INTRODUCING
Understanding Salters Science examinations

think first

Have you struggled with examinations even though your work in class is good?

Have you wondered why some students always do better at examinations than in class?

Do examination questions sometimes baffle and confuse you?

In this unit you will learn:

- how examination papers are structured
- how to avoid simple mistakes
- how to write better answers
- not to panic about unfamiliar story lines
- how to have a successful ending to your Salters Science course

After enjoying your Salters Science lessons, it's time for the final part, examinations!

This section of the book will help you to know what to expect when you walk into the examination hall.

Examination papers are very carefully constructed and pass through many checking stages before they are finally printed. They are not just a random collection of questions someone thought about a few days before the examination day. All the examination papers must match a very complicated grid system and follow a set of rules. This section will help you to understand how to answer examination questions and get all the marks you deserve.

Your choice

There are lots of Salters Science examinations:

- different tiers (Foundation or Higher Tier)

- different levels of study (Double or Single Award)

- separate subjects (Biology, Chemistry, Physics)

You will probably be taking Double Award Science.

Foundation or Higher Tier

The Foundation Tier examinations use questions targeted at Grades G to C and therefore the top grade you can get is Grade C. The Higher Tier examinations use more demanding questions targeted at Grades D to A*. Since these tiers overlap about half the questions will be the same in both tiers. When your examination papers have been carefully marked grades will be awarded. All GCSE examinations use these grades.

Grade A*   the highest grade

    A

    B

    C

    D

    E

    F

    G   the lowest grade

You will sit three examination papers, each paper lasts 90 minutes and is worth 96 marks.

You should only consider the Higher Tier if you and your teacher think you are capable of a Grade B or A. It is not a good idea for borderline Grade C candidates to enter this tier since many questions will be very demanding and be targeted at Grades B, A and A*. If you are thinking about Advanced Level courses in Science in the Sixth Form or College, the Higher Tier will be the one for you.

Talk it over with your parents and your teacher.

If you enter the Foundation Tier you will sit, Examination Papers 1, 3, 5

If you enter the Higher Tier you will sit, Examination Papers 2, 4, 6

Remember:

- All candidates carry out coursework, which is assessed by your teacher and worth 20% of the total marks.
- This information is about Double Award, so your final grade is doubled, for example Grades CC or Grades AA.
- Information required for the Higher Tier is printed with a purple background in this book and in the Year 10 book.

Single or double award

This choice will probably have been taken at the beginning of your course in Year 10.

In the Single Award there is less information to learn and understand but the standard is the same as Double Award.

There are only two examination papers in the Single Award.

If you enter for Single Award, Foundation Tier you will sit the same Paper 1 as for Double Award and only the first part of Paper 3.

If you enter for Single Award, Higher Tier you will sit the same Paper 2 as for Double Award and only the first part of Paper 4.

Remember:

- All candidates carry out coursework, which is assessed by your teacher and worth 20% of the total marks.

- In the Single Award you get only one final grade, for example Grade C or Grade A.

Separate sciences

You may be sitting separate Biology, Chemistry and Physics examinations.

You will sit core papers lasting 90 minutes and worth 100 marks, together with an extension paper lasting 45 minutes and worth 50 marks.

Overlap with other courses

The Salters Science course has been specially written to integrate with other courses such as GNVQ and CoA so you may be using this book to help you with these courses.

What are the rules for examination papers?

30 marks for Sc2

30 marks for Sc3

30 marks for Sc4

6 marks for Ideas and Evidence in Science

Total = 96 marks

Within the total of 90 marks for Sc2, 3, 4 there are 4 marks for:

'the quality of written expression'.

This means 4 marks are available for a logical, well written answer using scientific words.

EACH DOUBLE AWARD EXAMINATION PAPER

No more than 32 marks can be allocated to questions which can be answered in one or two words

Therefore about 64 marks are for answers using long explanations, descriptions or comparisons.

The questions will use:
1 Assessment Objective AO1:
    Knowledge and Understanding.
This will test your memory of facts and your understanding of them.
2 Assessment Objective AO2:
    Application of Knowledge and Understanding; Analysis and Evaluation.
This will test your ability to carry out calculations and interpret data as well as making judgements.

MATHEMATICAL KNOWLEDGE

In the Foundation Tier you are expected to find fractions and percentages, use averages, decimals and ratios, construct pie charts and plot graphs given the axes and scales.
In the Higher Tier you are also expected to change equations around, select axes and scales for graph plotting and use inverse proportions.

IDEAS AND EVIDENCE IN SCIENCE

This new study will test your understanding of the importance of various discoveries in Science. Historically significant discoveries, such as those made by Louis Pasteur as well as present day scientific developments such as the work of radio astronomers searching for life in other parts of the Universe, need to be looked at. Many other examples are given in this book and in the Year 10 Pupil book.

What are the rules for examination papers?

You will be expected to remember these equations!

1	the relationship between speed, distance and time	$speed = \dfrac{distance}{time\ taken}$
2	the relationship between force, mass and acceleration	$force = mass \times acceleration$ $acceleration = \dfrac{change\ in\ velocity}{time\ taken}$
3	the relationship between density, mass and volume	$density = \dfrac{mass}{volume}$
4	the relationship between force, distance and work	$work\ done = force \times distance\ moved\ in\ direction\ of\ force$
5	the energy relationships	$energy\ transferred = work\ done$ $kinetic\ energy = \frac{1}{2} \times mass \times speed^2$ $change\ in\ potential\ energy = \dfrac{mass \times gravitational\ field}{strength \times change\ in\ height}$
6	the relationship between mass, weight and gravitational field strength	$weight = mass \times gravitational\ field\ strength$
7	the relationship between the moment of a force and its distance from the pivot	$moment = force \times perpendicular\ distance\ from\ pivot$
8	the relationship between charge, current, voltage, resistance and electrical power	$charge = current \times time$ $voltage = current \times resistance$ $electrical\ power = voltage \times current$
9	the relationship between speed, frequency and wavelength	$wave\ speed = frequency \times wavelength$
10	the relationship between the voltage across the coils in a transformer and the number of turns in them	$\dfrac{voltage\ across\ secondary}{voltage\ across\ primary} = \dfrac{number\ of\ turns\ in\ secondary}{number\ of\ turns\ in\ primary}$

Spotting the science

When answering exam questions it is important to first ask yourself 'What does the examiner want me to do?' You will need to read the question carefully and think about the science involved. An examiner wrote the following sections of the book. In them he explains how he wrote the questions and how you should think about answering them. Try to answer the questions yourself on a piece of paper, and then compare your answer to the examiner's. If you get a question wrong read the examiner's comments again and try to understand why you got the wrong answer.

What sort of questions will I have to answer?

You now know about the framework of a Salters Science examination paper but what about individual questions?

Salters Science is different from other science courses because:

- Sc2, 3, 4 (Biology, Chemistry and Physics) is taught in an integrated way
- individual examination questions often involve parts of Sc2, 3 and 4
- scientific explanations are used to understand a variety of domestic, industrial and environmental situations
- individual questions often tell a story.

You should, therefore, not be amazed to see references about the Eiffel Tower, mummies in China or Anita going snorkelling. Examiners do try to make the questions interesting!

Just remain cool and focused.

Recently a question based on a solar powered hat appeared on a Salters Science examination paper.

If you had seen such a hat would you have wondered how it worked, what energy conversions were involved and how its performance could be improved? These were some of the questions asked about the hat.

In another question Bobby wanted to build a patio. Candidates had to explain the formation of a covalent bond, complete a diagram to show these bonds on a molecule of water and explain how the concrete hardened. The environmental impact of quarrying also required detailed explanation.

The purchase of a microwave was the basis of another question. Candidates had to explain its advantages over a conventional oven and why a rotating turntable was used. Candidates also had to calculate the cost of using the microwave for half an hour from the power of the oven and the unit cost of electricity.

This baseball hat incorporates a solar-powered fan for comfort as well as shade.

Examination practice

Two examination questions are printed on the following pages.

These questions:

- give you experience of straightforward as well as difficult questions
- show different types of questions
- show that questions are targeted at certain grades
- show how a story is developed through a question
- have marks awarded for the quality of written expression and an understanding of Ideas and Evidence in Science

Help from your examiner

After each question, there is a comment box. These comments from an examiner:

- highlight common mistakes
- contain acceptable answers
- include suggestions on improving your answers.

Background

The first question is based on an article in the *Sunday Times* in February 2001, although many newspapers carried this story. The article included a lot of factual information so it could easily be adapted for an examination question. Although it is based on Sc4, some understanding of respiration from Sc2 is required.

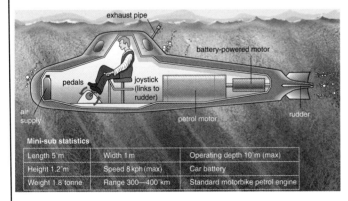

One man and his sub

Even in the often surreal world of inventions, Mikhail Puchkov's creation has to rank as one of the more bizarre: a pedal-powered one-man mini submarine. Surrounded by the masts of St Petersburg's Nautical Institute Yacht Club, where Puchkov is based in summer, the do-it-yourself submarine looks particularly out of place.

The authorities wondered how and why a Russian, Mikhail Puchkov, secretly built a mini submarine.

The second question is also based on a news item which appeared on TV and in newspapers. If you were going on holiday to Greece, Kenya or America in 2001 you would have been warned about this problem. Would you have understood the problem of deep vein thrombosis? Would you have thought about how elastic stockings could prevent this condition?

Of course in a real examination the questions will be new and you will not be given answers!

An enquiring mind is encouraged throughout the Salters Science course.

Now it's time for you to start thinking and to attempt the following questions.

QUESTION 1

Mikhail Puchkov built a mini submarine.

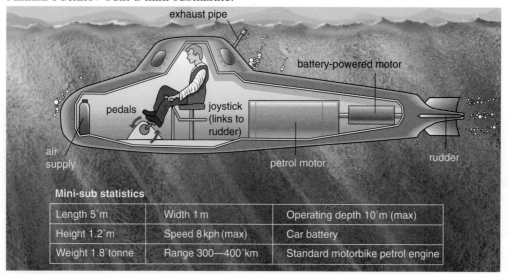

a) Various forces act on the submarine.

i) Choose from these forces to answer the following questions.

air resistance   buoyancy   driving force   friction   gravity

Which force will:

1   move the submarine forward? _____

2   cause the submarine to sink? _____

3   slow the submarine down? _____   (3)

EXAMINER'S COMMENT

This question is targeted at Grade G. Such a question would be considered a friendly way to start an examination.

There is no importance to the order of the words, they are always written alphabetically!

You must only use the words provided, if you make up other words such as **mass** or **engines**, these will be marked wrong.

The answers are: **driving force**, **gravity**, **friction**.

ii) Suggest why the submarine has a smooth shape.

_____

_____   (2)

EXAMINER'S COMMENT

The word 'suggest' is often used when there is more than one way to answer the question. Always look for the most straightforward explanation instead of some obscure way, since it will be easier to write about. The question is targeted at Grade E.

Remember the number of marks available and the number of lines drawn are vital clues as to how many facts your answer should include.

Always look at the previous part of the question. Here you can use some of the words from part i).

A simple explanation would be that it makes the submarine go faster because there is less friction, it is streamlined.

b) The submarine took $1\frac{1}{2}$ hours to travel 19 km.

Calculate its average speed to see if it was travelling at its maximum speed.

Equation used _____

Calculation

Answer _____ units _____ (4)

EXAMINER'S COMMENT

All Salters examination papers will contain some 'quantitative work'. This means some working with numbers. Here you are asked to carry out a calculation. This also requires you to know the formula for calculating average speed. Which calculations you have to remember for each entry tier is given in the specifications. You could ask your teacher for a list!

At Foundation Tier, examiners always comment on the poor quality of answers from this type of question, so get as much practice as you can. Common errors are:
- using the wrong formula, so learn them
- working it out incorrectly, so use a calculator
- writing down the wrong units, usually written as mph.

This type of calculation is targeted at Grade C.

Answers are, speed = distance/time

Speed = $\frac{9}{1.5}$

Speed = 6 km/h. A conversion to m/s is not required but is acceptable if correct.

Always remember to show your calculation. If your answer is wrong you can still get marks for the working out and the correct units.

c) i) Write down **three** ways Mikhail Puchkov used to make the submarine move forward.

1 _____

2 _____

3 _____ (3)

EXAMINER'S COMMENT

This type of question is limited to about 30% of the whole paper. Other questions test your understanding and require longer answers, usually with explanations.

It requires you to extract information from the diagram and is targeted at Grade G.

Answers are: man pedalling, petrol motor, battery power.

ii) Which way would be best for Mikhail to use when underwater for a long time ?

Explain your answer.

_____

_____ (2)

EXAMINER'S COMMENT

A common mistake is not to write down which way you are describing, leaving the examiner in doubt.
This is very careless and could cost you two marks. Always read your answer after you have written it to see if it makes sense.
The best way would be to use battery power since it does not depend on oxygen and will produce fewer problems with waste gases. Candidates could answer by ruling out the other two methods, for example petrol engine would use up oxygen and produce large amounts of waste gases.

iii) The submarine has a range of between 300 and 400 km. Suggest how this range would be increased.

_____

_____

_____

_____ (2)

EXAMINER'S COMMENT

Since the word 'suggest' is used, a wide range of answers can be considered. However, do not be tempted into outrageous ideas such as installing nuclear power!
Since two marks are on offer, it is usual to accept two different methods or one method with a good explanation.
Possible answers including using more oxygen bottles so the man does not run out of oxygen for respiration, or make the submarine take two men providing more pedal power, and so on.

Possible links between deep vein thrombosis and long haul flights have been headlines in many newspapers in 2001.

QUESTION 2

Doctors are concerned that blood clots may be formed when people travel long distances. Aeroplane passengers are advised to use elastic stockings. These help to keep blood circulating and prevent clotting.

a) Apart from preventing blood clots, why is it important for blood to circulate round the body?

_____

_____

_____ (2)

EXAMINER'S COMMENT

This question looks at whether you know what blood does and is targeted at Grade D and C. Take care with your answer because it asks 'why is it important?' Many candidates would simply write, 'To carry oxygen and carbon dioxide', without explaining why this is important. A better answer is 'To carry oxygen to cells which will use it to release energy from food'. Other possible answers would be to write about dissolved sugars or amino acids providing energy to cells or to carry hormones such as adrenaline so that the body can react to stimuli.

b) Humans have a double circulatory system

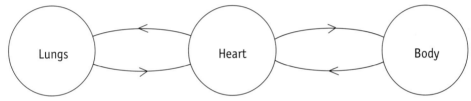

i) Draw arrows on the lines of the diagram to show the direction of blood flow. (2)

ii) Using this information, explain why the heart has four chambers.

_____

_____ (2)

c) From your knowledge of arteries and veins, explain how the elastic stockings would help blood circulation.

_____

_____

_____

_____ (3)

d) Read the following article about William Harvey.

William Harvey, the Detective Doctor

Two thousand years ago, the Greeks thought that blood moved backwards and forwards in the blood vessels. They believed that blood was quickly used up and new blood was made from food, water and air.

In 1628, William Harvey, a doctor working at St Bartholomew's Hospital, London, published a book about blood circulation. He showed that the blood moved in the blood vessels in only one direction. He also realised that the heart and not the liver kept the blood circulating.

William Harvey worked out how much blood was pumped out of the heart each minute. He then showed that this was far more than could have been made from food and water taken in. He concluded that the blood was not being used up but was continuously being moved around the body.

Choose **two** ideas the Greeks had about blood circulation. Explain how these ideas were changed by William Harvey.

Marks will be awarded for the quality of written expression.

_____

_____

_____

_____

_____

(4)

EXAMINER'S COMMENT

This question examines Ideas and Evidence in Science, a new part of the 2003 specifications. Some famous scientists are listed in the Specification Booklet for Salters Science and for the separate sciences. William Harvey is mentioned as an example in the new Biology specifications.

Also new is the awarding of marks for the quality of written expression in your answer. Older pupils and teachers may remember a similar scheme for Spelling, Punctuation and Grammar.

You should read the article at least twice to make sure you understand it. It may help if you underline or highlight relevant information. The question is targeted at Grade C.

Note that the word 'two' is printed in bold. This means that only the first two answers are marked, so think carefully before you answer. Many candidates do not plan their answer and write vague rambling answers worth only one or two marks.

Organise yourself and get a good grade!

Two marks will be awarded for explaining how William Harvey changed two ideas the Greeks had. For example, Harvey showed that the blood was not being used up but continuously circulated. Two extra marks will be awarded for the use of sentences, correct spellings and good linkage of facts.

Congratulations! You have survived these questions.

After attempting these questions you will have realised that:

- It will help you if you read the whole question before you attempt any answers; your brain will be 'tuned in'.

- Given a choice of words to use, you must use only them; you cannot make up your own.

- The marks available for a question are an important clue as to how much information you should write.

- In calculations you are allowed to use a calculator; so remember to take one into the examination.

- In calculations show your working; if your answer is wrong you can still get some marks.

- A pencil is useful when asked to draw information on a diagram; any mistakes can easily be corrected.

- A good answer requires planning; marks are available for the quality of your answer.

Now you can do your best in the final examinations.

Heinemann Educational Publishers
Halley Court, Jordan Hill, Oxford OX2 8EJ
a division of Reed Educational & Professional Publishing Ltd
Heinemann is a registered trademark of Reed Educational & Professional Publishing Ltd

OXFORD MELBOURNE AUCKLAND
JOHANNESBURG BLANTYRE GABORONE
IBADAN PORTSMOUTH NH (USA) CHICAGO

First published 2002

ISBN 0 435 629530

05 04 03 02
10 9 8 7 6 5 4 3

Writing team for revision of the Unit Guides:
Gill Alderton, Michael Brimicombe, Byron Dawson, Bob McDuell, Keith Palfreyman and Ann Tiernan.

Salters and Heinemann would also like to thank anyone else involved in the project (see the Year 11 Teacher and Technician Resource Pack for more details).

Project directed by Peter Nicolson

Edited by Alexandra Clayton

Index compiled by Paul Nash

Designed and typeset by Cambridge Publishing Management Ltd

Illustrated by Hardlines, Charlbury, Oxford OX7 3PS

Printed and bound in Great Britain by Bath Colourbooks, Glasgow

Acknowledgements
The authors and publishers would like to thank the following for permission to use photographs:

T = top *B* = bottom *M* = middle *R* = right *L* = left

1 Science Photo Library/Dept of Clinical Radiology, Salisbury District Hospital; **2** *T* Science Photo Library/Mark Clarke, *M* Science Photo Library/Jean-Loup Charmet, *B* Science Photo Library/R Maisonneuve, Publiphoto Diffusion; **3** *T* Science Photo Library/Richard T Nowitz, *M* Science Photo Library/BSIP Laurent/H. American; **4** *T* (inset) Roger Scruton, *T* Roger Scruton, *ML* Roger Scruton, *MR* Roger Scruton, *B* Science Photo Library/Hank Morgan; **6** *T* Science Photo Library/Jean-Loup Charmet, *M* Science Photo Library/Physics Today Collection/American Institute of Physics; **14** Science Photo Library/Keith/Custom Medical Stock Photo; **15** *T* Ace Photos/Roger Howard, *M* Science Photo Library/Martin Dohrn; **16** *T* Science Photo Library/Dr. Arthur Tucker, *M* Science Photo Library/Alfred Pasieka; **18** *T* Science Photo Library, *M* Science Photo Library/David Taylor; **19** Science Photo Library/Library of Congress; **20** Science Photo Library/Deep Light Productions; **22** Science Photo Library/Scott Camazine; **23** *T* Bubbles/Jennie Woodcock, *B* NHPA/Moira Savonius; **24** *TM* NHPA/B & C Alexander, *TR* Oxford Scientific Films/Mike Hill, *B* Chris Honeywell; **25** Oxford Scientific Films /Martyn Colbeck; **31** T Bruce Coleman/Steffan Widstrand, *M* Bruce Coleman/Kim Taylor; **33** Science Photo Library/Saturn Stills; **34** *T* Science Photo Library/L Shepherd, *M* Science Photo Library/Alfred Pasieka, **35** (both) Pete Morris; **36** NHPA/Moira Savonius; **38** Holt Studios/Chris & Tilde Stuart; **43** Science Photo Library/Martin Bond; **50** Popperfoto; **52** *TR* Environmental Images/Daphne Christelis, *TL* Environmental Images/Toby Adamson, *M* Science Photo Library/James Stevenson; **56** Roger Scruton; **58** Advertising Archives; **59** *MR* Science Photo Library/Pascal Goetgheluck, *BR* Popperfoto: The Book; **63** *T* Bruce Coleman/Jane Burton, *B* Environmental Images/Robert Brook; **64** *T* Roger Scruton, *M* Bruce Coleman/Roine Magnusson; **66** *T* Science Photo Library/CNRI, *M* Robert Harding/Upperhall Ltd; **67** Popperfoto; **70** Robert Harding; **72** *T* Oxford Scientific Films, *M* Oxford Scientific Films/Colin Milkins; **73** *TL* Science Photo Library/Martin Bond, *TR* Holt Studios/Nigel Cattlin, *LM* Holt Studios/Bjorn Ullhagen, *TM* Science Photo Library/George Post, *BL* Oxford Scientific Films/Martin Chillmaid; **76** *T* Environmental Images/Robert Brook, *M* Environmental Images/Robert Brook, *B* Press Association; **80** *T* Environmental Images/Vanessa Miles, *M* Wildlife Matters, *B* Roger Scruton; **83** *T* Holt Studios/Dick Roberts, *B* Pete Morris; **86** Holt Studios/Nigel Cattlin; **89** Holt Studios/Nigel Cattlin; **96** Colorsport; **97** Roger Scruton; **99** *TR* Science Photo Library/NASA, *BL* Science Photo Library/David Nunuk; **100** *M* Science Photo Library/National Optical Astronomy Observatories, *B* Science Photo Library/European Space Agency; **101** *T* Photodisc, *M* Science Photo Library/Frank Zullo, *B* Science Photo Library/Jack Finch; **102** *M* Science Photo Library/NASA/ Mehau Kulyk, *B* Photodisc; **103** *TL* Photodisc, *TM* Photodisc, *BM* Photodisc, *BL* Photodisc, *BR* Science Photo Library/Space Telescope Science Institute/NASA, *MR* Photodisc, *TR* Science Photo Library/Space Telescope Science Institute/NASA; **105** Roger Scruton; **107** *T* Science Photo Library/Mehau Kulyk, *B* Heather Angel; **108** Science Photo Library/NASA; **109** *TBR* Ace Photos/Berry Bingel, *BR* Science Photo Library/NASA, *BL* Rex Features/Peter Brooker; **111** Science Photo Library/Photo Library International; **112** *T* Science Photo Library/David Parker, *TM* Science Photo Library/Dept. of Physics, Imperial College, *M* Science Photo Library/ Dept. of Physics, Imperial College, *BM* Trevor Clifford; **114** Science Photo Library/European Southern Observatory; **115** *T* Science Photo Library/Mount Stromlo and Siding Spring Observatories, *M* (both) Science Photo Library/NOAO; **116** *T* Science Photo Library/NASA, *B* Science Photo Library/David Parker; **117** *T* Science Photo Library/David Nunuk, *B* Science Photo Library/ David Parker; **119** Science Photo Library/NASA; **121** *L* Science Photo Library/David Gifford, *R* Science Photo Library/D. Roberts;